UGANDA'S CHIMPANZEES

0 5 10 15 20 25 30 35 40 45 50 MILES

- - - - INTERNATIONAL BOUNDARY
• TOWN OR VILLAGE
——— ROADS WE TOOK
▨ FOREST KNOWN TO CONTAIN CHIMPANZEES
▨ NATIONAL PARK
▲ EXTINCT VOLCANO

SUDAN

WHITE

ALB

Murchison Park
VICTORIA NILE
RABONGO FOREST

Butiaba
Busingiro
SIBA FOREST
BUDONGO FOREST
MASINDI

BUNYORO
Dwoli
HOIMA

LAKE KYOGA

VICTORIA NILE

BUGOMA FOREST

LAKE ALBERT

CONGO

SEMLIKI FOREST

ITWARA FOREST
FORT PORTAL

KIBALE FOREST

RUWENZORI MTS.
RUWENZORI FOREST

UGANDA

KAMPALA

Queen Elizabeth National Park

Chapman's Farm
Kyarumba

EQUATOR
LAKE GEORGE

ENTEBBE EQUATOR

Katwe
Katunga
Mweya Channel

KASYOHA FOREST

Lake Nyamisigeri
KALINZU FOREST

MARAMAGAMBO FOREST

LAKE EDWARD

ANKOLE

MBARARA

LAKE VICTORIA

CONGO

KIGEZI

ISHASHA FOREST

IMPENETRABLE FOREST

Kisoro
KABALE

RUANDA

TANGANYIKA

Mt. Muhavura
Mt. Mgahinga
Mt. Sabinio

BUDONGO

The Natural History Press, publisher for The American Museum of Natural History, is a division of Doubleday & Company, Inc. Directed by a joint editorial board made up of members of the staff of both the Museum and Doubleday, the Natural History Press publishes books and periodicals in all branches of the life and earth sciences, including anthropology and astronomy. The Natural History Press has its editorial offices at The American Museum of Natural History, Central Park West at 79th Street, New York 24, New York, and its business offices at 501 Franklin Avenue, Garden City, New York.

BUDONGO

An African forest and its chimpanzees

VERNON REYNOLDS

PUBLISHED FOR THE AMERICAN MUSEUM OF NATURAL HISTORY

The Natural History Press, Garden City, New York, 1965

Text and endpaper maps
by Lili Cassel Wronker

Forest profile diagrams
by Stephen Kraft

Library of Congress Catalog Card Number 65-13101
Copyright © 1965 by Vernon Reynolds
All Rights Reserved
Printed in the United States of America
First Edition

To Frankie

Acknowledgements

Many people helped to make our journey possible, and our stay in Uganda pleasant. I thank them all. I should also like to thank Captain C. R. S. Pitman, C.B.E., D.S.O., M.C., and Colyear Dawkins, for commenting on the manuscript, and David Kershaw for photographic help in Africa. I am indebted to Mrs. Rosetta Baskerville for her collection of Uganda folk-stories. Most of the book was written in a little summer-house belonging to Dr. and Mrs. Ucko, and I thank them for the use of it. Thanks are also due to the staff of the British Museum of Natural History for help in various identifications. Last but not least, thanks to my wife for her helpful criticism.

Contents

List of Illustrations		viii
Chapter One	The Reconnaissance	1
Chapter Two	Budongo: The First Seasons	35
Chapter Three	The Forest	71
Chapter Four	Creatures of the Forest	89
Chapter Five	Days and Nights	131
Chapter Six	The Social Life of Chimpanzees	155
Chapter Seven	Africans of Budongo	173
Chapter Eight	Tracking and Finding	191
Chapter Nine	Gorillas	215
Chapter Ten	Back to Budongo	229
Further Reading		250
Glossary		251

List of Illustrations

Figure 1   Map showing location of fig trees and cor-
           responding movement of chimpanzees   55

Figure 2   Map showing location of *Pseudospondias*
           trees and corresponding movement of
           chimpanzees   62

Figure 3   Forest profile of *Maesopsis* forest   77

Figure 4   Forest profile of mixed forest   79

Figure 5   Forest profile of ironwood (*Cynometra*)
           forest   80

Figure 6   Map showing location of *Maesopsis* trees
           and corresponding movement of chimpan-
           zees   241

BUDONGO

CHAPTER ONE

The Reconnaissance

We stepped off the plane at Entebbe with the whine of the jets in our ears. We had come four thousand miles in half a day. The contrasts around us on the airport were immense, but we were immune to contrasts. The clock showed noon by some African time, a hot African sun beat on the tarmac, black men of Africa walked around us, African elephants looked down at us from posters in the lobby, and as the plane taxied away and left us, a great silence, an immense inactivity was revealed all around, and we felt it rolling away on every side across that unknown land into whose centre we had plunged —Africa, and nothing but Africa for thousands of miles whichever way we looked.

Utterly staggering, when we thought of how long and terrible a task it was for Stanley, Baker, Speke, Livingstone to reach this very region. Their routes had differed from ours not only in that they travelled overland, but that the only one who arrived here from the north, Baker, had followed the wandering Nile. The route my wife Frankie and I had just taken, straight as a die for two thousand miles across the eastern Sahara and over the Sudan, is still beyond the capabilities of man on foot.

We had woken at dawn and from that first instant kept our

eyes rooted on the unbelievable panorama. First a sharp red
line had signalled the horizon, parting the sleeping land from
the empty blackness of night. Then a red eye had blinked open,
revealing a moonscape below: sand as far as the eye could see,
stained yellow in the morning light, with here and there the
long thin shadow, perfectly symmetrical, of a conical hill covered with blown sand. Looking down from our cool perch,
progress seemed infinitesimal. Sometimes a range of hills,
mountains maybe, casting enormous shadows, crept under us
in this grand spectacle. Hour after hour no river wound its
way below us, no path cut across the land, no cloud was in
the sky. Then, twice, we crossed the winding dark ribbon of
Mother Nile, drifting warm and lonely down below us. She
disappeared in a blue haze, and all was desert again. Meantime the sun turned from orange to yellow and the sand
became white. We crept on, our trusty Rolls-Royce jets merci-
fully keeping up their steady tune, rushing us through the icy
upper air, incredibly slowly, over that burning desert. The
shadows of the hills began to shorten.

The transition from sandy desert to desert scrub was painful.
The land began to darken and was peppercorned with thorn-
bushes, then turned into desert again. Dry watercourses suddenly appeared like systems of veins, then disappeared again.
Yet we made it to the dry grasslands of the Sudan. I looked
down upon the Nilotic tribesmen below, the Nuer and Shil-
luk and Dinka, whom I had studied from books in remote
London years before, and thought of the photographs in those
books, of their long-horned cattle and smoke-filled huts and
tall, lean, heat-resistant bodies and naked skins. All I could
see was tiny dots: huts. And I wondered idly why people lived
in such a barren land, and wondered, too, whether they were
standing down there with their hands cupped over squinting
eyes, looking at the silver bird with its white vapour trail making a line across their sky. What did they think of us, those
proud folk seven miles down below?

From grassy savannah to the richer savannah lands of the southern Sudan. Trees in abundance now, but rivers still dry. It is January, the height of the dry season, and fires are everywhere, glowing red and sending up pillars or walls of blackish smoke, turning the air beneath us into a dull purple haze. Reaching Uganda the lateritic earth turns red, the colour of Neolithic pots, and the land, as if in contrast, is green. We begin the descent. Roads are red lines between the fields of green. It is a promised land, it looks good. As we come down to a mere one thousand feet we can see delightful red-roofed houses with flower-decked gardens, and with a simple upending of the wing we turn and see the entire world turn to water below us, blue water on every side as far as the horizon, so much water we have to gasp at the quantity of it. Skimming across the surface of giant Lake Victoria, our wheels make contact with the clean white concrete runway and in big letters we read the magic word "ENTEBBE."

The ride from Entebbe airport to Kampala is by Volkswagen microbus. We gaze at the sights around us. We are not on one of those red roads we saw from the air—this one is tarmac—but on either side the grass-covered banks are of that same red soil. Every few hundred yards a great termite mound rises up. Through gaps in the roadside we see native huts flash by, with gaily dressed women sitting in front of them. Africans, the men in shirts and shorts, the women in dresses, both sexes with hair cut short, walk up and down the roadside; a few cycle. Around the huts stand groves of banana trees, their broad leaves shaking in the wind, and behind these are fields of maize. Every now and then there are brick or stone houses with tin roofs. And the whole scene, even the inside of our car, is enveloped in damp, humid air, reminiscent of a big glass hothouse. People move slowly, their teeth flashing in laughter as we go by; here is a life such as we have never known, a concept of living totally different from

our northern severity and speed, in keeping with the steady
hot climate of this summer land which knows no spring,
no autumn, and no winter. Topping a hill, we see before us
the white clock-tower at the entrance to Kampala, the vari-
coloured buildings beyond, the gleaming domes of white
mosques, and the red-brick Protestant cathedral atop its hill.
Kampala is built, as Rome was, on seven hills; its population
of 47,000 is half African and one third Indian, with some
3000 whites. Indians are everywhere as we pass through the
streets; they run the shops and open-air bazaars. Indians are
the mainstay of Uganda's commerce. Green bananas in great
bunches lie around us, tomatoes and avocados, dried beans,
dried fish, oranges, fruit of all sorts. The street is full of bicycles
and people picking their way past each other. There are hundreds of cars and there is a parking problem. We glimpse sell-
ers of tin kettles and coffee in small yellow bags, of jerry-cans
and tin funnels; smart clothes shops and stationers line the
main street which we cross, going uphill past a modern post
office to a big hotel, where our bus stops and deposits us and
our luggage on the main steps. This is it: the beginning. We
do not know a soul in all Africa. Has our crate arrived? Where
is Makerere? How does one find a taxi? Are there any taxis?
Who speaks English? In front of us, watching with amusement, sit three men under a tree with a huge collection of
drums, stools, ivory, ebony statues, and birds carved from
horns. Do they speak English? Probably not. And my camera
is in the sun: the film will melt. Look at that cloth that
woman's wearing! Are those vultures on that tree? A legless
beggar holds out his hand—I have only English money.

Slowly, our minds clear; we order a taxi in the hotel; it
takes us the mile or so to Makerere; on our left all the way
is a tree-lined gulley and every tree is filled with twittering
bats, hanging in huge clusters like dead leaves. The driver
charges me ten shillings, which is five times too much. We
enter a room, led by a charming African in a long green gown

like a night-shirt, and put down our bags. The place is ours, the windows covered in gauze. It is cool. The journey is over. There is nothing to do but sleep.

Frankie and I had come to Africa to study chimpanzees. This was the outcome of a long series of decisions plus a good deal of luck, determination, and hard work. And behind all that lay our interests—mine in anthropology, Frankie's in animal behaviour. We had both been undergraduates at London University, though not at the same time, and had both decided to do research, Frankie on rats, I on monkeys. We met, and got married, and planned this Africa project together, submitting it to the university as a worthwhile topic for research, as almost nothing was known about the behaviour of chimpanzees in their natural home, the African rainforest. Because chimpanzees are so closely related to man, it seemed to us important that an attempt should be made to find out something about this ape. We were fortunate enough to be given a grant covering our basic expenses. Now all we feared was that we should be unable to find any chimps. To know the answer we had to go to those very rainforests and start searching.

Kampala was having its January heat-wave. While still in England we had bought a Land Rover from a zoologist leaving Uganda, and on our first day we went to the garage in Makerere College, where it was parked. With pleasure I saw that it was a very sound vehicle and worth the $600 I had paid. A 1956 model, in good shape; all it needed was the top re-covered and a new plastic back window; the present one had become opaque from the ingrained red dust of up-country Uganda: a foretaste of things to come.

With our Land Rover we were mobile: Uganda was at our feet, or rather at our wheels. Dr. Niels Bolwig, who was to have been our supervisor on account of his great knowledge of and interest in primates, had unfortunately just left the

Zoology Department of Makerere five days before we arrived. He had warned us that this might happen, but we had hoped to see him before he left. Undismayed, we followed his instructions and drove over to Entebbe to visit Dr. A. J. Haddow, one of Uganda's finest naturalists, also a primate expert. He greeted us cheerfully and advised us to look at all of Uganda's forests before choosing a study location, but suggested that the Budongo Forest might be the best place to work. He then sent us over to Allan Brooks, biologist to the Uganda Game Department, who was tremendously hospitable and shared Haddow's opinion regarding the Budongo Forest. This information was important, for despite our efforts we had been unable to gather any clear information in England concerning the whereabouts of large numbers of chimpanzees in Uganda. Now we were hearing from people who had actually seen them and had a wide knowledge of local conditions. We visited the Uganda Forest Department's headquarters at Entebbe, where Henry Osmaston supplied us with maps on which he marked the position of Forest Department rest houses in each major forest, and gave us permission to use them; in addition he gave us names and addresses of forest officers to contact en route. Again, absolutely vital information. From John Blower, then chief game warden for Uganda, we obtained on loan camp-beds, a table, folding chairs and a collapsible bath, plus a wealth of advice based on years of experience. Back in Kampala, we collected our crate, the motley collection of government-surplus and electrical goods we had sent out from England by sea three months before. They had travelled well: the tape recorder was still working, no camera lenses were broken; but we detected a faint bad smell around everything, and as we delved deeper it grew stronger. Finally at the bottom we found a nasty mess adhering to our tent: somehow a rat had got itself squashed inside the wooden crate and had, over the sticky hot months of travelling the high seas in a hold, imparted all the essence of its decaying flesh to our precious tent. The smell of death was strong, it had permeated through all the folds of the tent in a yellowish blotch. We tried airing it, washing the affected parts in Dettol, spraying it with Flit, but still the smell remained. Impossible to sleep in such a smell, but there it was; we gave up the struggle.

One of the most important jobs in Kampala was to find suitable containers for our gear. We settled on metal boxes in the end: rat-proof, waterproof, unlikely to break open, and cheap. We bought two big ones and two small ones, each a different colour, and each with a padlock. For the fragile equipment I required one further box, which I had made to my specifications; it was of heavier metal than normal and very rigid, the inside was lined with foam-plastic mats throughout, the top was not hinged but lifted straight off, and a strip of rubber around the rim made it dust-proof and well-nigh airtight. It was double-padlocked, everything of value went into it, and it served us excellently the whole time we were in Uganda.

Finally we bought a Tilley lamp, a jerry-can, and a score of other last-minute essentials, succeeded at the third attempt in getting everything into the back of the Land Rover, and roped the load down. Exactly a week after our arrival we were setting off north-westwards on the start of our tour of Uganda's forests known or thought to contain chimpanzees. All of these forests lay along the western border of Uganda with the Congo. Our aim in visiting them was to make a reconnaissance of each in turn, to decide which one would make the most suitable study area.

It was an odd feeling, setting off that first time into the bush. We had no guide, no interpreter, no experience, just a map with a number of crosses on it. Behind us lay London, the plane trip, our brief period of acclimatisation in Uganda's capital. The months of preparation, lists of things needed, orders of priority, insurance policies, documents, tickets, the sheafs of correspondence—all were behind us at this moment.

Every day for the past six months had been planned, now we had no clear destination and no time of arrival: we could take any road we chose. Yet this open space ahead was the final lap, all else counted for nothing in comparison. It was a fine moment, looking out towards the unknown as we rolled out of Kampala. Somewhere there ahead of us (it seemed incredible!) were chimpanzees.

Along the roadside women with concave backs hoed the soil, or walked serenely with loads of vegetables on their heads and, as often as not, a baby slung on their backs. Men rode bicycles, generally with huge loads strapped to the rear pannier—a big bunch of green bananas or a giant gourd containing beer. Bush-fires blasted us; we stopped sometimes to watch insects fleeing before the flames—mantises crawling helplessly across the road to be taken by droves of swallows riding with the smoke. Children waved as we went by; for their pains we covered them in dust. We gave many lifts, all squashed in the front seat, mostly to Africans going a mile or two, but once to a white father, in a flowing robe of khaki drill, whose motorcycle had broken down. He told us of the difficulties of making good Catholics of the remaining pagans in his area, and of syphilis—the widespread curse of the land.

From time to time we stopped, to watch and photograph one of the big-billed pied kingfishers along the road on the telephone wires, always near water, looking like short-tempered brisk little businessmen with long cigars—or that handsome bird, the long-crested hawk-eagle, or a tree thick with nesting marabou storks, or a crowd of vultures in a field, or a colony of weaver-birds fluttering and twittering around their pendant nests. Near Hoima, in Bunyoro, a baboon ran across the road ahead of us. We decided to stay at the Hoima rest house for the night. It was beautifully situated, overlooking a sweeping valley and distant hills. The calls of Africans came across the valley, a drum-beat from a nearby school. Dust from the bush-fires filled the lower part of the sky, turning it purple as the sun sank towards the hills. Our camp-stove roared and we opened a first tin. Black boys and girls wandered along the road, a thrush-like bird sang, and distantly the crackle of the bush-fires could be heard. We had escaped from civilisation for the present at least; water had to be boiled; there were no fresh meat or vegetables to be had; mosquito nets hung idly above our beds. Night came and with it the shrilling of the cicadas; the Tilley lamp was lit; small bats scrabbled in the roof and left, one after the other in a long stream; a sickle moon lay on its back above the balmy air. Life was full of promise and unknowns.

Next day, after speaking to David Lyon, the local forest officer in Hoima, we covered the remaining distance to the Budongo Forest. Here we made for the lumber mill, where we met George Barrow, who at the time was acting manager. "Chimpanzees?" he said. "They kept us awake all last night, hooting and shouting just behind our house. Must have been dozens of them." It was as if he had handed us a nugget of gold. Looking back on it, our excited enquiries and desperate attempts to pinpoint the exact spot on the map must have amazed him. Not that madness is anything new among white men out in the bush, but this chimp fever must have been new to him. In order to steady our nerves, he kindly offered to put us up in one of the mill's houses. We hadn't yet seen a chimp, but we felt keenly that we were nearer than ever before.

Next day we set out to look for a man called Marco Okenyi, the local game guard, who was to accompany us into the forest on instructions from the Game Department, which were contained in a letter we had for him. His address was simply Nyakafunyo. We found this on the map and set off confidently. Having arrived at the exact cross-roads marked as Nyakafunyo on the map, we were a bit put out to find nothing but grass for miles on every side, with the forest lying contentedly in the background. However, after wandering around for a bit, we noticed a buffalo skull and horns mounted on a

piece of wood and vaguely remembered that this was a Game
Department sign. A slim path led back from the skull, winding its way into the grass. We ventured down it. After no more
than ten yards we emerged into a clearing with three huts,
some women and dozens of children in it. The children
screamed, both they and the women disappeared.

I tried one of the very few words of Swahili I then knew:
"Jambo!" meaning "Hullo." At first there was no reply. I then
enunciated the names "Marco Okenyi" and "Nyakafunyo."
A dog wandered across to sniff us; I put out my hand to stroke
it as a gesture of goodwill but it raced away in terror. So we
just decided to wait. It was the correct thing to do. In the
bush, waiting is often the best thing to do: it allows excitement to die down and things can take their own course in an
African way. Before long an old woman, holding her dirty
clothes about her, came out and looked at us with great curiosity, but showing neither anger nor fear. I smiled politely
and mentioned Okenyi's name again. She replied in a soft
voice, with no trace of effort, no movement or expression.
Frankie tried to find some of the sounds she made in the
Swahili-English dictionary but could not; perhaps she was
speaking Lunyoro? I smiled and smiled as more women and
children emerged. "English?" I said enquiringly, but none of
them knew a word. They laughed and we laughed. It wasn't
embarrassing so much as comic. The day was burning itself
away, and we had no idea whether this was the correct place or
not. Finally Frankie deciphered the word "tembo"—"elephant." That made sense. Marco Okenyi was away hunting
elephants. What time would he be back? "Time" was "saa"—
we tried it and they answered, "*Kumi na mbili*"—twelve
o'clock, which in our way of reckoning meant 6 P.M. With
many thanks and waves we left them, fairly confident that
we were on the right track.

In the evening we returned and met Okenyi, a tall stately
man with a broad smile and his top front teeth missing; we

gave him the letter. As he read it, his wives looking on with awe, I noticed he was holding it upside down. He folded it up carefully, replaced it in the envelope, and handed it back to me. All the time he was smiling, and I thought what a friendly sort of chap he looked. Fishing inside my pocket, I took out a black-and-white photograph of a chimpanzee. He scrutinized it carefully, then called to a couple of young men who had been in the background until now. They began to talk about it and the word they used was "soko-mutu," which we knew to mean chimpanzee.

Suddenly one of the young men, who was neatly dressed in a white shirt, long grey flannels, and black shoes, said, "Are you searching for chimpanzees?" His English was almost perfect. It was as if we had been struck by lightning. From that moment on all was plain sailing. He read the letter, interpreted everything beautifully, and said he would come with us next day. We arranged to meet at 7 A.M. to set out in search of chimpanzees. They had, it appeared, been heard by Okenyi that very day. The omens were good.

At dawn we set out. Okenyi was ready for us, and two men, who came from a village called Dwoli, came along too. Okenyi carried his rifle. We drove a couple of miles into the forest along a logging track, parked the Land Rover in the undergrowth, and set off along a foot track. We were in single file, the three Africans ahead of us. The morning seemed long and was chilly at first, but slowly shafts of sunlight reached the forest floor, more birds sang, and more insects warmed to life. We walked a mile or so in silence, then sat down to listen. We scarcely knew what to listen for: we had read descriptions of the hooting and screaming of chimpanzees, and had heard them in zoos, but how would they sound in the forest, far away? Every now and then I heard a strange noise, but the Africans said no. They sat about smoking, relaxed; we began by listening tensely in anticipation, but slowly grew fidgety and bored as the morning drew on and our watches pointed to midday. Once one of the men whistled and pointed up the track: we saw a plump crested guinea-fowl, a beautiful dark blue-green bird with a red throat, the size of a chicken, standing upright and looking at us over the grass of the track. He began feeding, and two others stepped out of the forest to join him. In silence they made their way along the track, pecking every now and then, until they disappeared round a corner. We had brought some food and we ate it; the men ate nothing. They explained to us that the chimpanzees had moved away out of earshot and that it was useless to wait. We were disappointed, doubtful now whether it would be possible to find any. They said one could never be sure of finding them; we would return home now and try again tomorrow.

Half way along the track Okenyi stopped and looked into the forest to our right; we followed suit. It was impossible to see anything. He continued looking and listening and we kept silent. Suddenly there was a piercing squeal, short and sharp, quite close to us, followed by a "de-dum . . . dum" as if someone had beaten a big drum. Something dashed off among the leaves. The Africans smiled back at us. "What was it?" I asked.

"That was soko-mutu!"

To us the squeal could have been anything from a pig to an elephant, but the drumming was, of course, the moment we thought about it, typical chimp behaviour. Contact had been made! But how to study such a creature?

The following day we heard them loud and clear almost as soon as we stepped out of the Land Rover. We were in the same spot as on the day before: they had returned. This time we headed off the track after a short distance, and had our first experience of walking through the forest proper. The tension mounted as we got nearer and nearer and their calls grew louder. We picked our way between the saplings, tripping occasionally to our infinite annoyance. Okenyi crept ahead of us, bent low; when we made a noise he looked back, his face intense with the searching, and moving his fingers up and down gently he whispered, "poli, poli"—"slowly, slowly." Suddenly he stopped, and pointed upwards and ahead. We could see nothing at all. I crept forward as he beckoned me. I followed the line of his arm. Still nothing. He took me by the shoulders and forced me into position. I desperately scanned the tree-tops. Then I saw. A big black hairy arm was plucking fruits and stuffing them into a broad pink mouth. Further back were others: we could hear them snapping branches. From time to time they called and the din was terrific. We edged forward to see better. One saw us and suddenly the whole area was filled with a different cry, harsher and shriller; there were chimpanzees everywhere, swinging about in the tree-tops, crashing from branch to branch, diving down into the undergrowth, and rushing off. I guessed we had seen ten at least, but I had been too impressed with their tremendous size and agility to count them accurately. As they ran off we heard them calling. We began to talk out loud again, laughing and joking as the enormous tension in us found release. As we talked, a fine rain seemed to be falling on us. We looked up and there, superbly placed dead above us, was a big adult male, placidly peeing on us and looking down. We moved out of his way before heavier bombardment followed. Then I settled down with binoculars in a comfortable crotch, and with Frankie making notes as I spoke, began a long and full description of him. Every now and then he moved to pick some fruits, or he watched us, or he looked out over the trees to where the others were now calling. He was a fine male, with a balding head and greying rump, but not old, as his powerful lithe movements showed. Later, we were to discover that a big male frequently stays behind, all alone, after the group he is with has fled. This one seemed completely fearless. We watched him until our eyes grew tired and our stomachs contracted with hunger. Then we left him there, walking away as silently as we had come.

On our way home we were in high spirits; for the first time we felt it might definitely be possible, by concealment and stealthy approach, to make a chimpanzee study here. Our mistake today had been to give ourselves away: we should have been less eager to see everything. We reached the track and were just crossing a stream when there was a crash in the trees and we saw a flash of a big creature leap to the ground, then it was gone. It was a leopard, which had perhaps been waiting for a duiker to come to the water. We were glad of Okenyi's rifle and remembered with a shock that he would not be with us if we returned here to do a long-term study; he had his own work to do.

That afternoon we all went to a local "duka" (general store) and celebrated over bottled beer, European variety. The English-speaking boy was a carpenter, he said, now unfortunately out of work. He asked us to try and find him a job and we promised to try. His friend was a roof-mender, also out of work; we promised to try for him too. Okenyi alone was one of those few fortunates with a job, and a good one too; but it was evident to us that he was a hand-picked man, an Acholi by tribe, a natural hunter and tracker. Significantly these qualities had got him further than education would have done. At dusk we went our several ways after exchanging addresses. The Dwoli men offered to help us if we ever needed help. We went to bed happy and exhausted, with the sound of the tree hyraxes in our ears. Next day we would head south to reconnoitre our second forest, the Bugoma.

We set off early, to cover as much ground as possible before the day heated up. A chill mist lay over the gently undulating country as we drove along. Here and there the land was blackened where a bush-fire had raged; rivers were dry; the red lateritic soil was baked hard under our wheels. We passed numerous small villages; sometimes a woman was sweeping the earth in front of her hut and stood up to watch us go by. Between these settlements Uganda's countryside was pleasantly varied, with the road winding between hills dotted with low trees, and a total absence of hedges or fences, the land here being mostly unused and unowned. As the mist cleared we stopped at a duka for a breakfast of bananas (sixpence, or seven cents, for a bunch of twenty) which we had spotted hanging outside the door. By midday we reached the forest and were heading up the Bugoma sawmill road towards the Forest Department rest house marked on our map. That road, incidentally, merits a word or two as being one of the worst we ever came across in Uganda. Ruts up to a foot deep went all along it from the timber lorries which plied to and fro, and now in the dry season they were baked hard as iron. The wheels of these lorries were wider apart than those of the Land Rover and so it was not possible to drive in the ruts. Nor was it possible to drive consistently to the left or right of them, because of logs and stones and other obstacles. This meant that every few minutes we had to "cross the ruts"—a hair-raising experience as the car assumed crazy angles and everything in the back flew about. We were thankful for the four-wheel drive, thankful for the thick metal girders of our chassis. No normal vehicle could have survived the beating our Land Rover took up that five-mile track. We suspected that it would be us, not the vehicle, which broke up first.

Arrived at the rest house, we finally located the custodian, who settled us in politely. The place was fine, except for the water, which was the remains of some ancient rain lying in a dirty yellow puddle at the bottom of a tank. But this was the scarce time for water, so we didn't complain, and Frankie set to work boiling it up for tea; it hardly needed any leaves. We asked the man, who spoke a little English, to see if he could find someone who would take us into the forest next day to look for chimps. He said he would try. Finally, before leaving us, he smilingly said we should close all the windows at night, for there was a leopard which prowled round the house; in the middle of the night I was forced to go outside for perfectly natural reasons, and it was a hair-raising experience.

The Bugoma differs from the Budongo in that the forest is not all in a compact slab, but consists largely of a collection of hundreds of straggling forest strips known as gallery, or riverine, forest. Between them are great stretches of elephant grass, which, at the time of our visit, was tall because it had not yet burned down, as it would shortly. Next morning our guide, who was called Xavier and spoke English, arrived. We drove along the road a little way and then, pointing to a faint irregularity in the wall of grass, he indicated we should drive in. I hesitated but he seemed confident, so, engaging a low gear, we went in. As I drove I could see nothing but the wall of yellow grasses falling like a wave in front of us. We were following an overgrown track, and occasionally for a few yards the grass was discernibly shorter, but there were times when I thought we were lost. He pointed to left or right, however, and seemed quite at his ease. Any hidden object, a log or a hole, would have given us a terrible jolt; we might even have bumped into a sleeping buffalo. Bits of the grass flew in through every crevice in the car; I watched with dismay as the wing mirror was wrenched off, and every now and then I got out to clear the debris off the bonnet. Suddenly, without warning, we reached forest and the grass ended abruptly. We jumped out and found we were still on the track, which cut clean between the trees.

After a while we heard chimpanzees, faintly, and set off in pursuit. Now the differences from Budongo made themselves felt—this forest was a mass of ants, little black biting tree-ants which fell onto us and bit until we smudged them out, and the undergrowth was thicker and more strewn with lianas: it was altogether inferior forest, we felt. But we had to press on. After an hour or more we were closing in on the calls; Xavier now said we should wait, and as we did so a group of chimpanzees hooted and drummed quite close to us. He insisted we should continue waiting. We sat still, our eyes trying to pierce the bushy wall ahead. The calling grew louder; it was as if a music-hall audience, shrieking with delight, were coming straight for us. Suddenly it stopped, and there was a pause, followed by a rustle in the leaves ahead. Something moved, darkly between the leaves. A space that had been sunlight blackened suddenly and then was light again. We searched, feeling the eyes of the chimps gazing at us, but unable to see them—it was an eerie sensation and we held our breath. The silence seemed interminable; were the chimps still there? More and more we began to suspect they had melted away on spotting us, fading out noiselessly among the trees. Or were they still sitting there, ten yards away, watching curiously? Suddenly I saw a movement—a long black arm reached upwards out of a clump of bushes, grasped a sapling, pulled, and up popped the head and shoulders of a chimp—a young one, curious and bold. We looked at one another. He scratched. An ant bit me on the neck; I let it. Then there was a sound to the left, the young fellow leapt down and was gone, there was a crashing of leaves and a booming of drums and a single wild call, and the silence of the forest set in again, quite empty and different from that tense silence when we and the chimps had been gazing towards each other, we blindly, they with inquisitive black eyes.

We asked Xavier about the drumming sound and he explained, in broken English, that there is a special drummer chimp, who carries the drum, but it is closely guarded so that humans will not see it, and the drummer always goes last. Additionally, he pointed out to us strange circular areas on the forest floor where the brown leaves had been flattened and not a sapling grew. Here it was, he said, that the chimps danced and drummed and shouted when they had their carnivals. We later discovered similar patches of apparently trodden-down soil in the Budongo Forest, when we returned to work there, usually in a circular area about ten yards in diameter. What they are remains uncertain: the sleeping places of elephants? Despite our extensive studies of chimpanzees in the ensuing months, we never saw a dance in such a glade.

We tried the Bugoma a few more times in different places, but without success. It wasn't a pleasant place to work: the canopy was not dense enough to make it really cool underneath and the ground was a constant tangle. Probably it did not support a very large chimpanzee population, for we never heard another call.

We decided to move on to the Kibale Forest, near Fort Portal, further south. Everywhere bush-fires were raging. Now we were on the foothills of the Ruwenzori Mountains, and when for a moment the smoke-filled dark air parted, we could see distant blue peaks covered in snow. Impressive green fields surrounded us, fields covered in low bushes only a foot high— these were the tea plantations; huge bright-red exotic flowers hung from shrubs, swallows and rollers and bee-eaters swept through the air, and all through the heat of the day the great mountains lay like a shimmering wall to our west.

The Kibale Forest was more like the Budongo than the Bugoma: tall trees, continuous forest for miles with cool shade underneath. We saw a group of redtail monkeys which jerked their heads and squeaked as we went by, and suddenly our tracker, who was taciturn most of the time, pointed into a bush and we saw a mongoose, frozen on a branch in alert concentration. It leapt away. Later he showed us a chimpanzee nest, but although we spent three days wandering through the forest, at the northern and southern ends and in the middle, we only once heard chimpanzees and failed to find them.

We pressed on southwards, following the line of the mountains, our next halting point being Chapman's Farm, at the southern tip of the Ruwenzori range where a road ran up into the mountains to a height of seven thousand feet. On our way we went through the Queen Elizabeth Park at its northern end, seeing buffalo, kob, water-buck, wart-hog, baboons and elephants. We came out of the park plains again and started climbing, finally reaching a village called Kyarumba, where the road petered out. We were now among the Bakonjo tribe. The people clustered around us as we pulled up, and directed us to the village chief. He was dressed in a clean shirt and trousers and was seated in a chair, talking to two other men when we arrived. We were impressed by the dignity of his face and manner and talked to him with genuine respect. A boy of eighteen or so, named Richard, interpreted for us. The chief, who was not a Bakonjo himself but a Mutoro, gave his permission for us to put our tent up outside the beautifully woven wicker fence of his compound; next day Richard would accompany us up the road, no longer used by cars, to Chapman's Farm and on up into the mountains to look for chimpanzees. He was doubtful whether we should find any.

As the excitement caused by our arrival died down, and the children and dogs and goats departed, we looked around us. Ahead a great valley fell away with mountains towering beyond. Above our heads a flock of weaver-birds twittered at their nests. A green, red, and blue lizard watched us from a branch. We began to pump up our inflatable tent with our rickety car pump. Only two children were allowed to watch us; they were the chief's; the rest were hustled away. These two stood close, their eyes filled with wonder as we took out our pots and pans and paraffin stove. A heron winged its way across the silent air of the valley. Richard asked us if we needed anything, handing us a bowl of cool fresh mountain water. Evening came and the air grew chill: we were high in the mountains and felt like kings.

At dawn the three of us set off for Chapman's Farm. Was it just a name, or was there really a farm and a Chapman? People had told us that there was, and yet the road was wholly overgrown. Turning a bend in the track, we saw a huge dilapidated structure of great poles covered in rough bamboo thatch, and instantly three big alsatians, chained to stakes, set up a violent barking at us. We stood still, uncertain what to do. As we waited, the figure of Captain Chapman appeared from the log house. Finding we were fellow countrymen, he came forward to greet us. He was old and his clothes were shabby. He invited us inside.

As we surveyed his home, we marvelled at the toughness of his spirit. He lived on chapatties (the round "pancakes" which are the Indian equivalent of bread), and these he made from cassava flour. There were also oranges, bananas, the occasional chicken, and cups and cups of tea made from tea-dust. His larder hung from the roof by a wire to stop the insects crawling in. The roof had been damaged by a terrible storm and needed repair. The floor was paved with flat stones—how had they got here? A number of ancient, tarnished copies of the *Tatler*, the *Sphere*, and the *Illustrated London News* lay on the table, and a letter, years old. He had come here, he told us, from the Far East, thirty years back. He had searched Africa for water, a stream strong enough to drive a wheel, and here he had found it. There was nothing but the stream when he arrived. He had built a mill to grind the cassava into flour, people had come for work, he had paid them wages and they had grown rich, building a village. Everything was due to him. Then cassava flour began to lose favour. . . .

He took us to the mill, where he still produced a bag or two of flour every now and then. Proudly, he took a handful of the pure white stuff and showed it to us: we murmured approvingly at its lovely texture, for truly it was beautiful flour. But it was cassava and apparently no-one wanted it. Now the local men were getting cheeky; talk of independence was in the air. They wanted his mill and would drive him out of it. They would force him to pay taxes. They were stealing his property: all his spoons had gone. He would go to Brazil and start again. The dogs barked and looked vicious; he went and talked to them. "The 'Watu' [Africans] don't get away with much these days," he said. "If I hadn't bought the dogs I should have nothing left now, they would have driven me out long ago."

At times he raged, at times he was wistful and envious of our youth, at times he was cheerful and hopeful of life in distant Brazil. He pressed us for information about Brazil, as we sat drinking his tea out of grimy cups that had long since lost their handles. What little he had he gave us, a piece of cold chapatti, a drink of pure orange juice, squeezed from the fruits within minutes of picking.

In bygone days when he first arrived he strode up the mountains behind the house, but not for the past ten years. In those days, yes, he had seen chimpanzees up there in the forest, but not now. We would have to go far, he said, and the going would be tough. Still, he wished us luck and saw us off, and as we started up the path we waved farewell to him, unable to analyse our feelings. His was the most isolated existence we had ever known.

The climb up to the forest—montane forest this, and the first we had seen—was a steady forty-five degrees, and as the morning grew hotter we grew steadily weaker. Richard bounced ahead with the fitness of a mountain goat and kept telling us it was not far, not far now, but the mountain kept its steady angle ahead of us. Some Bakonjo villagers from higher up met us on their way down—small, musty-smelling folk in dirty rags with huge baskets on their backs, supported by a thong around the forehead. The baskets were full of cassava roots going, perhaps, to Chapman's mill, but more likely to the market at Kyarumba, where they would be bought for boiling and eating in the traditional manner, like potatoes. Some maize and bananas went past us too. On and on we clambered, blind to the great variety of wild flowers which covered the mountain, growing desperately tired and thirsty. Then the slope began to level out and we found ourselves on top of a ridge. Ahead of us was a valley, on the other side of

which was a village with vegetable gardens and, above this village, the forest. We sat down and looked at it bleakly, across
the valley. We should have to climb down five hundred feet
or so and then all the way up again, and up a good deal further on the other side. Distantly we heard music coming from
the village: it was a strange yodelling, wailing sound, rising
and falling, eerie. "Why are they singing?" I asked Richard.
"They are not singing," he said, "they are crying for the spirit
of a man who has died."

We staggered to our feet and began the descent. On the
way we met a man whom Richard asked about chimpanzees.
He said they were there, above the village. At the bottom was
a stream: we risked the water and drank, and stood in it until
our feet were cold. Above us, as we climbed, the strange wailing cries of the mourners became louder. Each voice burst out
loudly, the note becoming higher at first and then trailing
away down an unfamiliar African scale. Finally we reached the
village, sweat pouring into our eyes. The wailing went on unabated, and was coming from a group of people sitting in
front of a hut; just below them a man was standing in a half-
made grave wielding a hoe, and the rhythmic note of his hoe
striking the stony ground added to the strange rhythm of
the mourning chant. Those not concerned with the mourning
looked at us with enormous interest; few white people had
been here since Chapman came up thirty years before. This remote village perched on the mountainside had always lived
as it did now, renewing its mud-walled houses as need arose,
re-thatching with banana leaves, making mats and baskets,
tilling the soil always at an angle of forty-five degrees.

These were among the poorest people on earth, we realised,
and they seemed content. But according to Richard, the Bakonjo were not content, for their lowland neighbours, the Ba-
toro, were oppressing them, extorting high taxes from them,
and keeping them out of the jobs which existed down below
in the towns. Indeed, we had been impressed with the differ-

ence in wealth and hygiene (judging by smell) between the two peoples: no sooner had we started to climb these hills than the white shirts and shorts of the lowlands disappeared, replaced by dull brown rags. The Bakonjo were now, said Richard, planning to revolt against their Toro overlords, they would rise to the last man, sweep down to the plains and kill the enemy. I wondered as he spoke how it would be possible to mobilise all these scattered hamlets in their remote fastnesses, felt doubtful about the success of such a revolution.

Above the village the path wound on for a short distance to the fields below the forest. A woman dressed in torn sacking told us that chimps had raided her maize field earlier in the morning and had retired to the forest. Our hopes were high and we crept on up that remorseless slope. We passed fields of yams, their green leaves poking out of the mounded soil, and fields of cassava, which looks like a tall shrub above the ground; some cassava roots which had been picked were left lying on a big stone to dry out white. Ahead, the last field of all, at the upper limit of cultivation, was a field of maize. A woman, naked above the waist, was working here and for ten cents, we bought a few young cobs, which we ate voraciously, drinking down the milky fluid in them. We took some more and gave her fifty cents, which was five times what she wanted —she had no idea how much the maize was worth to us, and was not so bold as to ask a high price. She then showed us some cobs which had been bitten into and then thrown down, about a dozen in all; this was what the chimpanzees had done, and it was clearly that very morning, for the maize was fresh. Leading off from the field towards the forest, Richard found their track. We followed it carefully, and soon found some very liquid feces, which were nevertheless identifiably chimp. A little further on was the peel of a ripe wild banana and the big black stones from inside it. As we went on, we found more of these: the chimpanzees had breakfasted on fruit and cereals!

The trail was very clear, and must have been often used. As

we reached the edge of the forest we were climbing on all fours, the slope was almost vertical in places. Richard showed no fatigue and helped pull us up the vertical bits. Inside the forest it was cool. We went on painfully slowly for about an hour. There were nettles up here and we kept getting stung. Not a call from the chimps, but we found a small group of nests in the trees, beautifully sited, with a long view over the valley to the plains beyond. Finally we stopped, utterly exhausted. The chances of catching up with the chimpanzees seemed remote indeed, as we were making so much noise and moving so slowly. So we decided that Richard would go ahead to scout about while we recovered our strength. Half an hour later he returned having found nothing. We were disappointed, but relieved that the climb was over. Even chimpanzees, we were beginning to feel, weren't worth the effort we were putting into this goose-chase.

We came down by a slightly less ferocious slope, using sticks, as the Bakonjo did, to prevent us slipping. I remember we passed through a small patch of dense *Podocarpus* trees, like giant yews, deliciously fragrant underneath, and cool. We now, for the first time, looked around us at the extraordinary variety of wild flowers, and took in the splendour of this Ruwenzori scenery. We had been up to eight thousand or nine thousand feet, the chimpanzees clearly went up still higher, perhaps as far as the tree-limit at ten to eleven thousand feet, but probably not far beyond as there would be no food. As for the sheer physical effort of climbing, they, with their powerful long arms, would have no difficulty. We reached the village again: the wailing continued. Two children ran past us with strange wicker frames stuck with leaves covering them from head to toe—a ritual connected with the mourning? Distantly across the valley a drum summoned with its regular beat. We went on down. It was nightfall when we arrived at Kyarumba.

Next day we got off to a lazy start, dragging our stiff aching limbs as we packed our gear back into the Land Rover. We

said our good-byes to those charming mountain folk and especially to Richard, for whom we promised to try and find a job.
Our destination was Mweya Lodge, in Queen Elizabeth Park,
where we intended to stay the night and look around a bit at
the wild game. Down out of the hills we rolled, and were soon
on the level plateau of Uganda again. We crossed the equator,
passed Lake George, shimmering to our left in the distance,
turned finally into the road to the lodge, passed the sign saying
"Elephants have right of way," photographed some of these
noble beasts by the roadside, and finally reached Mweya at the
Kazinga Channel. For the past fifty miles now the land had
been flat and barren and yellow—the quantities of game it supported amazed us. At the lodge the only accommodation available was too expensive for us; our grant was not designed for
such contingencies. So, with dusk approaching and menacing
black clouds in the sky, we made for a cheaper rest house at
nearby Katwe, on Lake Edward.

Katwe turned out to be a big ugly fishing village of tin huts,
smelling horribly and teeming with people and litter, the first
such place we had seen—doubtless a result of the flourishing
fish industry which had brought crowds to live there. We drove
through, hoping the rest house was a good way further on,
and just as it was growing ominously dark, a sandstorm blew
up quite suddenly, filling our mouths with grit as we asked the
way; luckily we found a rest house and arranged to spend the
night there. We were not a moment too soon. As we stepped
out of the car, a few heavy raindrops splashed on the bonnet,
and in an instant the most colossal storm unleashed itself,
thunder and lightning and thick heavy rain. Unfortunately
this rest house was none too waterproof and we discovered a
torrent of water pouring through the roof onto the beds we
were to sleep in; we dragged them away. The wind was now
terrific and seemed about to blow the house away; for a quarter of an hour it raged and then slowly, reluctantly, things returned to normal. It was dark by now and we could hear our

voices, the clatter of water on the tin roof had stopped; we lit the Tilley lamp and made a makeshift supper. Everything was soaking wet, neither the Land Rover nor the house had kept out the storm. There were puddles on the red tiled floor: we left them to soak away. Looking at our ruined beds we got out the sleeping bags and prepared for a damp night.

Next day we discovered we had come to the wrong rest house. The one to which we had been directed was up the road, situated on a promontory running out into the lake, with a glorious view over basking hippos and elephants, with pelicans and plovers and the scavenging marabous among them and a troop of vervet monkeys in the low trees. To this house (which had a splendid roof) we now moved.

All afternoon we listened to the snorts of the hippos basking down below us in the bay, and the wild cries of fish-eagles came to our ears. A flock of pelicans flew gracefully overhead, and one of marabous. Elephants came to feed on the bushes by the water's edge among the pure-white yellow-billed egrets, wading in up to their bellies for a cool-down. Wart-hogs, buffaloes and water-buck could all be seen through binoculars along the lakeside in the shimmering distance. And yet despite all this, Africa hung heavy and slow as she always does in the heat of the afternoon. The band of vervet monkeys with their olive bodies and black faces filed across the peninsula of open ground, going from their low trees to the water; some were mothers with young clinging below them. As the sun went down, the hippos' grunting rose to a muffled roar and we several times ran to the window expecting to see one on the verandah, but they were always down at the edge of the lake below—closer to the land now than they had been, and less compactly grouped together.

As the light failed, we saw the first one raise his bulk out of the water and begin to walk with a certain dogmatism in his regular steps, left-right-left like a clock-work toy, away from the water and inland along his path to the trees where the vervets were now roosting, and beyond to the stubbly grass somewhere in the far distance. Night fell and a full moon lit the wondrous scene from our bedroom window, as hippo after giant hippo emerged from the lake and started his own particular trek along his own path, doubtless to his own feeding ground beyond. What was most amazing was that the parched plains, which at this time of year were dry and yellow, could support so large a hippo population: each beast must have had to travel miles in its search for forage.

Up before dawn next morning and at Mweya in time for the Kazinga ferry which leaves at 7:45 A.M. On our way to Mweya we nearly have a nasty accident when a hippo, returning late to his watery daytime home, suddenly finds us approaching in our Land Rover between himself and the lake. He makes a dash for the water and, just as we are about to collide, thinks better of it and swerves off alongside us. At Mweya we meet our game guard, named Dario.

Crossing the Kazinga Channel we see cormorants, pied kingfishers, and herons. On the far side we drive for half an hour across the plains of Queen Elizabeth Park, yellower than ever in the morning sunlight, until we reach trees and a lake of unbelievable loveliness, as one imagines all Africa to be, Lake Nyamisigeri, with a flock of pelicans on the far bank, crystal water, abundant trees overhanging the water's edge, and, reminiscent of Kipling's *Just-So Stories*, a hippo blowing bubbles in his grandmother's ear.

On again, and midway through a grassy level plain we meet a lone man, walking with a musical instrument called "lokemu" for company; it is a small square box with pieces of metal of various lengths on top of it, and on it with his thumbs he patters out a delightful melody.

Three crowned cranes greet us at the Congo Road; we follow it, straight as a die and yellow as the dusty plains on either side. Amazing—we see occasionally huge herds of topi antelope up to a thousand strong standing and staring at us from a goodly distance as we beetle past with our trail of dust half a mile long; kob, too, and water-buck: what do they live on?

We pass by a limb of the Maramagambo Forest, in Queen Elizabeth Park, where chimpanzees are known to live, but this is not our objective; Dario motions us on. Finally we reach a game camp at the southern end of the park, where another guard joins us. We shall make for the forest along the Ishasha River, which marks the Congo boundary, twenty miles ahead, and there look for chimpanzees. Each man has a spear. As we see the forest to our right, the guard beckons me to leave the road and head for the trees; a half-mile or so of apparently level grassland separates us from the forest edge. Bump! In a twinkling we jolt to a halt, poised at a crazy angle downwards into the earth. Where all had been level dry plain, the front wheels are now bubbling downwards into a little patch of bright emerald-coloured grass: a disguised and overgrown water-hole. We are out in a moment with the aid of four-wheel drive and a good push from the men. We know now how the topi survive, and we know how to avoid plunging into more holes, so we weave our way between potential emerald danger spots and finally arrive near the forest, where we get out and walk.

Dario and his friend go first as we enter the cool green depths. He says the elephants here are "kali sana"—very wild, very cruel. And no sooner have we stepped inside the forest than the men stop dead still, poised and listening, then, beckoning to us, they point, and there between the leaves ahead of us, we see the head and ears and long white tusks of an elephant looking straight at us; almost imperceptibly, as we watch, he fades away and is no longer there. How impressive he had been, much more a killer here in the forest, where his bulk is hidden and he can melt away, than out on the plains where he is visible a mile off.

We move along the river, finding two or three old buffalo skulls, heavy, their giant horns still full of menace in this disembodied state. A colobus leaps away overhead. We see chimpanzee nests, old ones by the looks of it. A redtail monkey. Behind us the elephants shriek; fresh elephant dung lies on our path. Huge footprints can be seen in the mud at the water's edge where they have crossed this swirling brown muddy river, with its periodic tangles of fallen trees and lianas and dark-brown rotting vegetation. A bird repeats its single piping note, another its cadence; a woodpecker cackles; leaves crackle underfoot. Our two rangers, with their six-foot spears held at an angle, march steadily ahead of us. Two herons drift over the river, looking about them as they follow its winding path away into the trees.

It is afternoon. Our stomachs, which have had nothing but an egg and a slice of bread to work on since 5 A.M., remind us that we have far to return. The guard's hunch was wrong: we have not heard a chimp all day. The men are disappointed but we require no explanations. Hungry and beginning to tire, we peg our way back to the Land Rover waiting in the sun and begin the seventy-mile drive back to Mweya and Katwe.

The following morning we left Katwe to look at our last forest, the Kalinzu, a huge compact block of trees adjoining the Maramagambo to the north-east—a bigger forest than any other in Uganda. We saw it first from the road. As we left the endless level plains of the park and crossed its eastern boundary, hills piled up abruptly, one above the other in a steep escarpment, and from the road as we climbed we glimpsed ridge upon ridge of forest-covered up-and-down country to our right, as far as the eye could see. Unlike any other forest we had seen, the Kalinzu was nowhere level, but scarred throughout with valleys and intervening ridges. In this it resembled on a small scale the Impenetrable Forest, still further south, which we were to visit on a later occasion.

But the Kalinzu was less inaccessible than it looked. With valuable *Parinari* as its dominant species of tree, a Sikh-run sawmill flourished there, and to this we now made our way along an excellent road. At the mill we met the manager, a burly Sikh named Singh of rather terrifying appearance, with a big black beard matching his Wellington boots, blue trousers, a white shirt, and a red turban. He welcomed us with twinkling eyes and flashing teeth, listened attentively to our story, assured us the forest was full of chimpanzees, and asked if we would like to see his guns. We assured him yes, but stated firmly that we were against the killing of chimpanzees, at which he looked puzzled. So we began again the story of our quest. Whether he believed it or not, he burst out in a hearty laugh, at which we were extremely relieved, thumped us on our backs, and promised to see to everything for us.

And he did; his generosity was enormous and embarrassing. At first he gave us an empty house, but then he decided to put us in his father's house with his father and nothing we could say would deter him. It was a lovely wooden house, but not as lovely as his own, which was an architectural marvel in expensive woods and glass, perched on a hilltop, overlooking the mill in the foreground and the forest behind. We were invited there for supper, which was a delightful curry served by his wife almost on her knees and leaving the room immediately she had put it on the table. For amusement he dandled his young son, whom I called "she" for over an hour on account of his pigtails—a living plaything with big, darkly made-up eyes and a look of unbelievable innocence, like an angel. After supper we sat replete in comfortable arm-chairs while he told us of his son who was studying at the London School of Economics, and we told him all about London. He himself was intelligent, tough, and shrewd. We sipped our whiskies and looked out over the vast breathing forest under a tropical topsy-turvy full moon and, midway through the evening, the distant calling of chimpanzees floated to our ears. A good omen.

For breakfast in the old man's house we had curried potatoes and chapatties and tea mixed with milk and sugar *before* boiling. Then we set off to meet the tracker who had been laid on by the manager. He was not there. After waiting for half an hour we had two alternatives—to go to the mill and ask for a replacement, or go into the forest, of which we had no map, alone. We feared that if we did the former the man, who probably had not understood his instructions, would be in dire trouble with Mr. Singh, so to avoid this we did the latter.

Taking careful compass bearings we set off into the trees, towards the spot where yesterday we had heard the chimps. The forest was pleasant enough to walk through; we descended a cross-cutting ridge on the far side of the level forest, crossed a river by a tree-bridge and heard, not far away to our left, a group of chimpanzees calling. Taking a new bearing we headed straight for the spot. Sometimes it was necessary to take a slightly circuitous route to keep on the high ground and not get into the valley, where the vegetation was denser and there was water. We paused on a log to listen. Ahead of us the trees moved: we seemed to have stumbled right on them. Stealthily we moved a little closer, and saw a big black shadow in the saplings—it looked more like a gorilla than a chimpanzee. We waited. They had moved on a short way. We crept forwards again, but they were not to be seen. We kept edging forwards. Suddenly I was aware of two big forms in a tree just below us down the slope. They were chimpanzees all right; one was white with age all over its back, and this one was being groomed by another big black one. They had not seen us, and we had a splendid view of them. To be on the safe side we hid in some long grass. Suddenly a young chimp climbed a small tree right beside me. We kept perfectly still as he went, watching out of the corners of our eyes. We could

hear the pad pad of his hands on the bark, and see the inquisitive searching look on his face as he gazed up into the
branches looking for fruits. He didn't see us, but when he got
to the top and settled down he did, and came tumbling out
of the tree noisily, but the others took no notice. There were
more chimps about but we could not see them; they seemed
to be feeding on the ground. We kept our binoculars trained
on the two big ones. Slowly, the old grey-back got to its feet,
walked away in leisurely fashion, and descended the tree. The
big black one turned to face us: he had until now been overlooking the valley. He sat there lazily, legs dangling, pulling
in the odd fruit and eating it. It was only a question of time
until he saw us, we felt, and we were right. The light may
have glinted on our lenses; suddenly he sat upright, moving his
head slightly to get a better view. He was a splendid male,
big and tough. We waited; so did he. Meanwhile the others
must have moved off, for there was no sign of them. We grew
tired of waiting; he did not. We stood up, slowly; he stayed
still, watching us. I was glad we had not come to kill him: it
would have been a cinch. Instead I got out the camera and
took his photograph; it was the first photograph of a wild
chimp I had ever taken and one of the first ever taken of a
chimp deep in its natural forest habitat.

Gently we turned our backs on him and walked away. At
the last moment before we disappeared from sight of him, I
turned round. He was still there, immobile, keenly watching
us with his gruff, intelligent eyes.

Elated with our success, we set off on our return bearing.
It was early afternoon. We rounded the ridge we had come
along and crossed the river by our tree. We climbed the opposite side and then, inexplicably, found ahead of us another
valley which had no right to be there. The compass needle
pointed us inexorably onwards, and yet I knew there was no
second valley. We marked our position and cast about for
some sign of our earlier track. Nothing. We thought of going

back to our return starting point and tried to get back but could not find the way. We turned round again, determined to follow the compass bearing. Around us the trees now took on "familiar" or "unfamiliar" appearances. "I remember this tree!" I would call out confidently. "We've only got to go a bit further this way and we'll see the road." There was never any road. We walked in circles. We did everything wrong. We got hot, angry, and desperate. Finally I got seriously alarmed, and Frankie began to cry. We still had not done the one and only correct thing in these circumstances—to follow the bearing accurately and absolutely, and this we now did. It plunged us deep into this valley we knew nothing of; we waded along its swampy bottom through shrubs which rose above our heads; frogs croaked around us and we felt that snakes were slithering away as we approached. Suddenly I had an idea: what if we had come in along a ridge, and on our return had followed our bearing a few yards too far to the left or right? We would then walk straight into a valley running beside the ridge along which we had come in. To test this idea I left Frankie in the bog below and struck off up the right-hand valley side at right angles to our bearing. The hunch was right; there was the Land Rover a hundred yards away. "It's there! We've made it!" I shouted to a grief-stricken Frankie below. And as if in answer, a single low chimpanzee hoot came through the trees.

We stayed on another day, going in this time with the tracker, who was called Sobiri, but we did not find our hairy friends again, although we heard them. By now we were up to our ears in curry. The hospitality of the Singh family was unbounded: we scarcely had time to write up our notes in the evening before someone was waiting to accompany us to the big house for dinner. The father, we discovered, had a passion for religious wrestling matches, and showed us booklets about the champions, with photographs of huge-chested Sikhs in turban and pants, and details of their appetites:

one ate eighteen beef-steaks at a sitting, while another would consume a whole ox between dawn and dusk. His own knowledge of English was rather small, and his books were all in Hindustani. At night he sat glued to the radio, an immense and costly piece of equipment which made sounds like a drain; this was apparently Radio India broadcasting from Bombay.

The morning after the second day we left to return to Kampala. We hoped perhaps to come back for another look at these fine Kalinzu chimpanzees. But in fact we never did.

CHAPTER TWO

Budongo: The First Seasons

Twenty-seven miles from Masindi along the road to Butiaba, there is an S-bend as you follow around the bottom of a hill rising to the left; to the right is nothing but tall trees. At that point you are between Busingiro Hill and the Budongo Forest. At the beginning of the S-bend a track leads off left up the hill. Go up this track and on your right you will see a garden full of flowering shrubs and trees, white, red, yellow, and blue blossoms in glorious abundance. At the end of the track there are forty steps, and lizards, some with blue or orange heads, sit on them. These will scamper away into the dry leaves as you walk up the steps, or dash into crevices in the rocks after jerking their heads at you a few times. At the top of the steps you will see a beautiful white-painted bunga-low and when you reach its verandah and turn to look back, you will see a canopy of leaves stretching lazily away to the horizon.

That was how we first saw the house which was to be our home for the next eight months, for we had now settled on Budongo as the best forest for our study. Coming from Lon-don, we had not thought such a thing possible, and so we had brought with us a big tent, but neither of us had any doubts about the advantages of brick walls and a tin roof, even over the best canvas made by man. So when David Lyon, the local forest officer at Hoima, had offered us the use of his rest house for the period of our stay, on condition that we left room for visiting forest officers and other officials for whose use it was intended, we jumped at the idea. And when we saw the house we jumped again, for joy.

Except for lizards the house was completely empty and, being made of brick with stone floors and plaster walls, it was pleasantly cool. To the right, as we approached the verandah, was a door leading to three big square rooms, each with glass windows and inner ones of insect mesh which we swung stiffly open; behind the second and third rooms was a bathroom with a wash-basin and *bath!* Left of the verandah was a single room and behind it a scullery and larder. Beside the house to the left was an outhouse: the kitchen, containing a large decrepit Dover range, while to the left a little way up the hill were the servants' quarters in another building, and to the right was the lavatory or "choo"—a typical long-drop of the type found throughout East Africa, with, like every other, its own particular insect fauna and dominant species. (At Bugoma this had been a long-legged hopper, at Kalinzu a small winged insect on the walls, at Katwe a vivid red cockroach; here it was a common buzzing fly.) Two tanks, fed from the gutters around the corrugated iron roof, supplied the house with water. One was of metal and stood at the corner of the house nearest the kitchen, and the other was of stone and stood at the other rear corner; the former was empty and the latter nearly so, for this was still the dry season. In later months these tanks flowed over at each torrential downpour.

Behind, the hill rose up, covered with a tangle of dry elephant grass and dispersed small trees. While Frankie set about organising the domestic side of things, I plunged off through the grass towards the top of the hill. It was a nasty hot journey and the hill was higher than it had appeared, also the grass had burned near the summit and my clothes and hands and even face were soon charcoal black. But the view from the top was worth it: the outline of the forest's western rim was discernible, and beyond it the escarpment with Lake Albert glittering down below and the hills of the Congo rising misty and blue on the far side. A kestrel hovered above me as I watched, and over the forest a pair of vultures was wheeling, or perhaps they were eagles. A little wind rustled in the leaves of the cork trees.

Down below again I was greeted by the clatter of pots and pans, the roar of the paraffin cooker, and the smell of a delicious stew which Frankie had made out of our stock of tins. We discovered an old lawn beside the house to the right, shaded by lovely planted trees, and down below the garden was a ruined garage, with roof intact but half its wooden walls missing, and, ludicrously, a termite heap two feet high in the middle of the floor. We were to see that heap grow to four feet in the period of our stay.

By evening we were settled in and felt it was home already. The last of the three rooms was designated our bedroom and living room; the single room to the other side was to be our dining room, and the other two big rooms could be left empty. Having so little furniture (two camp-beds, one table, and two chairs), we had no space problems. Once, faintly, we thought we heard chimpanzees in the forest below but could not be sure. A francolin rasped away below the house, bulbuls chirped like sparrows among the flowering trees. As night fell a ghostly bird looking like a nightjar flitted about and answered me as I imitated its call. Fireflies with their intermittent glow flew noiselessly through our garden. As we sat out sipping beer, cicadas, stick insects, mantises, and moths came to our verandah, lured by the light of the Tilley. The hyraxes began their piteous grating chant, like lost souls in the black forest below. It was all part of a pattern we would come to know very well: the pattern of living in the African bush.

Our objective was very clear: to observe as much as possible of the behaviour of our chimpanzees. What was a good deal less clear was how to set about it. There was no-one to ask. Below us lay the shimmering green leaf-ocean of Budongo in which, somewhere among those 135 square miles of trees, our quarry was to be found. No amount of waiting would help; we had to get into the forest and start searching. But looking out from our cool, comfortable verandah, over the acres and acres of continuous canopy which lay dreaming before us as far as the horizon, we felt utterly inadequate even to begin the task. We were tempted to wait until we had found a tracker, someone who knew the forest well and, perhaps, knew where chimpanzees were to be found. But it might be a week or more before we discovered a good man, and, after all the delays and preparations, we wanted to make a start.

Even though we had got lost, briefly, in the Kalinzu, our technique there had been sound—we had simply made the mistake of not adhering to our compass bearing. If we kept carefully on course, there was no reason why we should not succeed in seeing chimps here, even before we got a tracker. All we needed was a burst of calls to direct us, and as it turned out we did not have to wait long. Our second evening on the verandah we heard the familiar howling and hooting in chorus from the forest below—it drifted up to us tantalisingly, weak at first and then in louder and louder bursts, while around us the evening grew silent and still. The sound was intensely disturbing; in a strange way we felt something in ourselves almost at bursting point, we wanted to reply or to go down to the forest at once and join in the mêlée. It was as though we were being left out of something we wanted very much to join in—the feeling one has hearing dance music or jazz calling one through a darkened Soho doorway.

We took a bearing on the calls. Frankie cooked a camp supper and we ate it to the music of the chimpanzees; then, though too excited to sleep much, we went to bed early.

It was still dark—no glow as yet from the eastern horizon opposite our window—when the alarm rang. By torchlight we dressed, and Frankie groped her way to the kitchen to put on a kettle for tea. Six o'clock saw the first faint streaks of orange creep up beyond the forest horizon. The verandah was chilly as we sipped our tea; the last hyraxes called from the gulf of blackness ahead, whose upper rim gleamed red like fire and showed up the silhouettes of tiny distant trees against the sky. As soon as we could see our way down the steps we got into the Land Rover and headed off down the bumpy path to the bottom of our hill, then along to the left until we came to the beginning of a track leading into the forest, which we followed towards the Bubwe River. The previous evening we had calculated with ruler and map that this would bring us close to the position from which the calls were coming.

Going down the track we immediately entered the forest and found ourselves in inky night again. A civet stood transfixed in our headlights, its eyes like stars. We bumped along, making, it seemed, a terrible noise, stopped at the river bridge, switched off and listened. At first there was a silence, as if every creature around had fled. Above the trees the sky showed, a faint dull indigo. It was cold. Once something rustled in the leaves behind, and an owl called. We were, in fact, too early: the day had not yet begun down here inside the forest. It was fully half an hour before daylight penetrated to the forest floor, by which time we were cold and wondering whether we might have grossly miscalculated the chimps' position. So we drove half a mile further down the track to its junction with another smaller one leading off to the right. As we got out of the vehicle we heard them instantly. The compass showed them to be almost due south. Parking the Land Rover in the tangle at the track's edge, I grasped the "panga" (long knife) and faced south, feeling confident that I could tackle this African jungle and its inhabitants.

Frankie, I think, was rather scared that first day as we

pushed our way blindly through the giant trees, guided by the intermittent calls which continued to tantalise us. But she kept it to herself and, at all events, preferred to be with me down in the forest rather than wait behind and worry at our home on the hill. In point of fact, I can say without lying that I was not scared on that first day, but it is equally true that this was largely due to false confidence. In the early days I did many risky things through plain ignorance rather than bravery. As time passed and we experienced more, talked to people with first-hand knowledge of the forest, and learnt from our tracker, I came to realise the dangers inherent in what we did, wandering unarmed through the forest. Frankie, on the other hand, took an almost opposite psychological course. She commenced our operation almost too scared to get out of the Land Rover and was crying heartily before the first day was out, wanting me to carry a gun—even our little .22 would have given her confidence. But as the days went by and we remained uneaten by leopards, unstampeded by elephants, and unbitten by snakes, her calm and confidence grew.

We crept at first through long elephant grass at the side of the track, then entered the forest proper. To our left a sudden hoarse bark startled us. Frankie thought it was a leopard because she had heard that they coughed; I had other views but I kept quiet and looked at the trees. It came again, and I pinpointed the area and watched until something moved, and then I realised that our progress had aroused a sentinel baboon in the trees at the forest edge. He barked again, and again. So now the whole area knew it had intruders; the rasping repeated bark was like a burglar alarm we had set off, alerting every creature with ears to hear, spreading the news of our arrival. Too bad; we would rather have been unannounced. But the chimpanzees called again and we realised they might well be out of range of this baboon.

We pushed on, tracking south, myself cutting a path, Frankie close behind with compass in hand. We had made a vow that this time there was to be no manoeuvring and losing ourselves; it was to be straight in, and then straight out again. Every now and again our chimps called ahead, but never, it seemed, much nearer. My right arm started to ache from lack of panga-practice, and also simply because the panga was new and had not been sharpened to the fine sword-edge necessary to deal neatly and efficiently with the branches and creepers and thickets. Added to this was my sheer lack of skill with the knife, for, as I later learned from watching our tracker, every cut must be worked out momentarily beforehand, the strength of the blow necessary to do the job without wasted effort, and the angle of the knife to cut the branch diagonally through. I was hacking about and so I quickly got tired, and in addition my knuckles kept getting grazed and were soon bleeding merrily. Nor did our avowed aim of sticking to a bearing permit us the luxury, later taken for granted, of detouring round exceptionally dense thickets, so when great prickly hedges of shrub blocked the way ahead, I simply cut my hand to shreds making a hole big enough for us to crawl through.

But we went straight on along our bearing, too busy with scratches, twigs and ants in our hair, fallen trees to crawl under or clamber across, and occasional gaps to squeeze through, to think about possible dangers. Every forest animal —bird, beast, and reptile—must have heard us coming that day.

And then came the first blow to our method—calls came to us through the trees and checking on the bearing we found they were ten degrees to the east of south. This could only mean that the chimps were moving. Moving away! Follow! Faster! We had been going for two hours now and were sweating profusely; without pausing, we pressed on along the new tack, hating the chimpanzees, cursing ourselves for the utter stupidity of abandoning civilisation for this. And now, having changed our course, something in us kept saying that every

step was taking us further into a mess we should never find
our way out of; but another, blinder force said to press on
now, after such effort already spent, and clinch it.

We clinched it all right. Gradually we closed in on the
noise. We moved in carefully at the finish, not using the panga
but creeping and crawling forwards, edging from behind one
big tree to another. A huge volley of hoots and hollers and
howls and barks shattered the silence just ahead of us, and
the ground shook with the noise of a deep bass-drum—
"de-BOOM, de-BOOM BOOM BOOM." The noise was tremendously
exciting. Ahead we saw branches shaking, and then we saw
chimps, two or three youngsters playing together above, and
we heard others snapping branches as they fed nearby, and
saw an adult female who swung into full view before disappearing into the foliage again. Observation was good, and
Frankie was filling the pages of our pocket book. Then I saw
an adult looking back at me, straight into my eyes. I merged
imperceptibly with the tree trunk we were crouching behind,
kept hidden for a few moments, and then ever so gently allowed one eye to peep out again. The chimp was still looking straight down the lenses of my binoculars, lips slightly
apart, its whole body tense and alert. I faded away into the
leaves for a full minute but it was no good; others had noticed
the behaviour of the first and were looking now to see what
the source of interest was. We kept carefully hidden and
waited, moving slightly to see round the other side of the tree.

Here there were a number of chimps in another tree, who
had as yet no idea of our presence. At first I tried simply to
count them and whisper to Frankie, whose pencil was poised
for action, the sex and approximate size of each animal. But
they kept moving and disappearing into the leaves, making
this extremely difficult. One or two were sitting still or feeding
—an old grey-backed male was facing away from us, sitting on
a branch and doing nothing; on a branch beyond I could see
an adult lying stretched out lazily on his back, one arm grasp-

ing the branch above, while another chimp sat upright, industriously grooming his head. Further to the left I spotted something pink through my binoculars—it was a female "in heat," with a great glowing behind. I focussed on her carefully. She moved a little way, pointed her behind towards another chimp—a male—and looked back at him. There was movement through the leaves, a huddle of chimp, and a squeal.

Then Frankie touched my arm urgently and said, "Look!" Close ahead in a sapling not ten yards away to our right was a young adult, clinging to the thin trunk with hands and feet, staring at us fixedly. In a strange way, his square-boned face was like that of an Iroquois brave, and it had the same menacing quality. At first he chewed leaves and then looked at us, chewed some more and looked again. Then, suddenly, he let out a harsh, shrill bark—a different sound altogether from the hoots and howls we were now used to. He began to swing the whole sapling from side to side, looking at us, then he leapt off it to the ground and immediately clambered up another even closer to us. And now the most amazing sight, one I shall never forget, appeared before us—so incredible that note-taking was inconceivable. Chimp after chimp after chimp climbed up the saplings all around us, and up in the trees above our heads more and more of them appeared. They barked and shrieked with harsh cries. They shook branches. They leapt about. The whole forest seemed alive with them. The chorus grew louder and louder. Frankie blanched. I asked her if she felt all right, tried to comfort her by a show of calmness, but she could not hear me even though I shouted. The chimps meanwhile kept closing in; one hung from a hand to get a better look at us. Then, suddenly, there was a great crash just behind us. Swinging round, I saw a branch, big enough to knock out a man, settling onto the forest floor, a result of the wild leaping about in the tree-tops overhead.

At this point there was no doubt that Frankie wanted to

beat a retreat. Persuaded by reason, knowing there are no
authentic reports of chimps attacking adult humans unpro-
voked, I suppressed my emotions and watched carefully to see
what would happen next. Drumming boomed close beside us
but we could not see the drummer in the tangle of undergrowth. The shouting swelled again and I timed a chorus,
which went on for six minutes continuously, lulled for ten
seconds, then swelled again. But now even reason had to give
place; every moment the chimps were getting closer and more
audacious—it was as if they were working themselves up into
a frenzy, and I really felt one of them might boldly strike at
us if we stayed. A look at Frankie's tear-stained, imploring face
settled it: we could find out more later on. For today we had
had enough. So, turning from the crowd of apes, we crept
back the way we had come.

Those chimps had been angry with us, I think, very angry,
with a kind of mob anger. We had provoked them by our
impertinent curiosity and insistent presence. Their display
was, however, tinged with the same curiosity that we felt towards them. For we had white faces, and white faces are not
often seen deep in the forest. What were we? Perhaps the
crowding chimps had been as eager to find out more about us
as they had been to drive us away from their feeding ground.

If the morning had been exhausting physically, and the
midday period with the chimps mentally so, the afternoon
was sheer hell. For with that stubborn blindness with which
only a vast forest can stare you in the eye, the reverse bearing
refused to lead us back to the forest edge. We hacked our way
on for hour after hour, reasoning and cursing. At three o'clock
we hit a trace going from west to east—temptingly it lured us
with the promise of easy walking and we succumbed, thinking
that it must surely lead to the track we had come in along,
which we knew ran to our west. The lovely trace ended, after
half a mile, in a neat mound of earth with a stick in it. We
tried retracing our steps but could not be sure how far we had

come. I couldn't recognise anything although I kept searching for the white slash-marks of the panga. So we just pushed north where we thought we might have been, knowing that eventually by going this way we must hit the smaller track at some point. We emerged at last; looking around, we found we were about a quarter of a mile too far to the east, nothing worse. It was hot outside the forest in the tall grass, and the menace of Africa lay all around us in the dull silence of the afternoon. But there was the friendly patched green canvas roof of the Land Rover; we dragged ourselves into it and set off for home.

Bumping wearily homewards we made a resolution. The chimps could call; let them. We *must* find a tracker, a good one, someone to wield the panga, someone who might know ways and means of getting to the chimps faster than we could. Next day we enquired of the local forest ranger, who took us to a hut where we met Manueri.

Manueri is the name of our tracker. He is about forty but there is no great certainty in it. He comes from the northern foothills of the Ruwenzori and is a Bwamba. He is roughly my height (five feet ten inches) and stout about the middle from much drinking. His arms and legs are steely-tough, his walk is determined, his clothes are rags. But above all else, Manueri has a huge, wild, gleaming, wicked smile.

He is tough, he argues with me about wages, he argues about the hours I want him to work, he compares his miserable ill-luck working for me with the good times he used to have in the Forest Department and at the mill. He mentions bonuses, overtime. I pay neither, just a flat rate day in day out. He talks about Sundays as if they were holy to him, and I agree to pay him double, at which their holiness vanishes.

Manueri and I do not know from the start whether we will get along together. He needs the money, and jobs at his age are normally unobtainable. I need a good tracker and he

knows the forest from fourteen years of working in it and
drinking illegal spirits in it. His is the low paunch of the
drinker, not the high one of the gourmet. His stomach has
never distended very far: he eats to keep alive and he lives to
drink. From the start I like him, because of that smile. But
between smiles he looks sour and unfriendly. He has the air
of a man playing his cards very carefully, when the stakes are
very high.

He smiles and throws his hands up and says he cannot, cannot work for so little money, it is ridiculous to expect him to.
I explain the work is simple, he will get increases. I am wary
at this stage of offering him more; anyway I can't afford it.
Finally we shake hands, it is agreed. He asks me to wait while
he gathers his possessions.

Manueri's possessions are as follows: one blanket, one mat-
tress, and two cooking pans. Apart from these he owns the
rags he wears (rag-shorts, rag-shirt, rag-jacket), a hut which is
dirty, dark, and empty, and a field. Owning the field makes
him sound rich, but not so—everyone around here owns a
field and most of the land is unowned. Land cannot be
bought, the chief gives it to those who need it. Manueri
goes into his field and uproots some cassava, which he places
in a dirty piece of sack—another possession. Then we walk
with the bundle to the Land Rover and start the drive to our
house, where he will now live. Eight months later I shall be
bringing him back to this same hut for the last time, and
parting from him will be sad.

For I did not know it then but I was to get to know Manueri very well. I was to spend the greater part of seven days
each week walking with him in the forest, waiting for his arm
to cut the path, following his vanishing form as it twisted
along animal tracks I could scarcely see. I was to rely on the
tattered sight of Manueri's shirt with its great holes, and his
shorts falling apart at the seams, learn to respect his silence
when he felt like it and to join in his joviality. His body

smell was strong and was only outmatched by the smoke of his terrible cigarettes. The pad-pad of his soles on the ground ahead as we walked, always in single file, was immensely reassuring. When he pointed, it was worth looking as a rule. Certainly, we had our ups and downs and I lost patience with him every now and then, especially when he was drunk and failed to turn up for work; but for his part he bore with me very well—there were many times when he could have laughed at me for my ignorance but he never did. He always tried to explain.

And he was an excellent interpreter when I had to talk to other people, for I came to understand his Swahili perfectly, using all the clues of his facial expressions and gestures as well as the words: I got to know the emotional content of what he was saying. This I could not do with other men, whose dialects were different or whose conception of Swahili was based on another mother tongue than Manueri's and was thus totally different. In these cases Manueri would come to the rescue and put things in phrases he knew I could understand; if he said it one way I knew I could answer jokingly, whereas if he said it another way I knew there was something serious at stake. This was a great help when we later employed several chimp spotters, who came to me every now and then with a variety of complaints. "Je nasema . . ." Manueri would always start—"That [man] says . . ." and so on. In the end we always hammered it out, whether it was a question of getting wet, or "ov-time," or whatever.

Manueri had some strange ideas, and some very sensible ones. Among the strangest was the idea, fixed quite immutably in his mind, that Europeans (some of them, at any rate) actually eat Africans. I ridiculed this but he just put tongue in cheek and said it was true, although nowadays there were very few cannibal whites left.[1] Far more sensible were his views on

---

[1] We later discovered in John Beattie's book *Bunyoro* what could well be the origin of this idea. It seems that at the time of J. H. Speke and

clothes. He bemoaned the passing of the barkcloth era. Every now and then, in the forest, he would point at a tree with his panga and say "Hi nyakatoma"—"This is a barkcloth tree."[2] We would gaze at it with respect. For, as Manueri pointed out, when the people wore barkcloth they put on fresh, clean clothes as often as they needed them, whereas now that barkcloth was no longer prepared, they were forced to buy their "shirtsi" and "shortsi" with money they had not got, and so they walked around in dirty rags feeling ashamed. "You should return to using barkcloth," I argued, but he laughed and replied that it was women's work, that he had left his wife and child behind in Bwamba fourteen years ago.

We always felt sorry that his family was split. He was such a likeable chap, but who knows what lay behind his decision to leave home and family, to travel and seek work? He said he would return one day when he had saved up enough for the bus fare, but so far he had not saved enough. I asked whether he expected to find his wife waiting for him and he said "Yes." I suggested lightly that it was a long time and she might have found another man, and he said "Labda"—"Perhaps," saying the word entirely without conviction either way. We felt he ought to return home when his working days ended—that his old age would be miserable as a bachelor away from home, with no income—not enough money even to buy a bottle on a Saturday night. He said he would start saving.

But what use was saving for Manueri? He did save once, with the following results. We had paid him his wages one Saturday and he had gone off gleefully—to spend it all, we imagined, on a vast weekend binge. So we were not greatly surprised when he failed to show up on Monday morning. He

J. A. Grant's journey through Bunyoro, a hundred years ago, the Baganda, anxious to foment trouble between the Banyoro (their traditional enemies) and the Europeans, spread stories among them that the Europeans were cannibals and given to the most terrible deeds.
[2] *Ficus natalensis.*

finally arrived in the evening, and I prepared the usual admonition and threats, but his story was different and—though he related it with a smile—tragic in the extreme.

"Saturday evening we drank—a very great amount of beer. I knocked into two bottles of 'waragi' [liquor]—my head was just floating away. I went to sleep. However, the men of the chief knew I had money left over from my wages. They came to my hut Sunday and took me away to prison in a Land Rover. I was in prison all of Sunday. Today they returned with me to my house and I paid them my taxes from the money I had saved. I owed them poll-tax for two years, the money was still not enough. I have lost all my wages and still I owe them money." And as so often, his story ended with the plea "Mimi nataka r'vance, bwana—shillingi tano tu"—"I need an advance, sir, only five shillings."

Of course, he should have kept up his poll-tax payments. Every man who owns a house has to pay poll-tax to the local chief, everybody knows that. There is only one snag: it is an impossible sum for those who have no work. The chiefs use all sorts of means to obtain their dues, once they know a man has some money. For example, where wages are paid over a table, their henchmen stand around and pounce on men who owe them money the moment the wage-packet is handed over. To counteract this, men who owe tax pretend to be sick at pay-time and get their money later. Word must have got to the chief's men that Manueri had money saved up and so they had grabbed their man. Now his savings were gone and he had nothing again.

He accepted this thing of the poll-tax with a cheerful fatalism which we already knew in him. Manueri was too old to grieve. Life was, for him, a light-hearted battle of wits in which the most subtle and skilful man won. This was evident in all our arguments, which frequently centred around wages or hours of work: if he could prove his point in logical argument he expected (and got) his way, and if I convinced him on a technical point he conceded the battle cheerfully enough. Hidden malice and the sulks were qualities he lacked entirely.

He was a hard man to surprise and I can only remember one occasion when he was absolutely thunderstruck. All of one day we had been close to a large group of chimpanzees, tape-recording their wild choruses. He had watched my antics with the Grampian microphone as I stuck it at a suitable angle in a branch, he had seen the magic eye of the machine flicker as the sound of the chimps rose to a crescendo, he had seen me twiddling knobs and had spent the whole day in enforced silence, seeing me frown and put a finger to my lips whenever he coughed his awful, chesty smoker's cough. He must have wondered what it was all about.

When we got back home that evening we waited until after supper when the hill was all in darkness and then, placing the tape recorder in the middle of the lawn, I switched it on at maximum volume and retired to our table to await results. In no time the night air was filled with screams and hoots, as if a great tribe of apes was sweeping up the hill. Frankie and I sat nonchalantly sipping beer. In a minute a hesitant form appeared, knife in hand, mouth agape.

"Wapi soko-mutu?"—"Where are the chimps?" asked Manueri.

"Chimps? What chimps? Asleep in the forest, I suppose."

"Can't you hear chimps?"

"*Hear* chimps? No—you must be drunk."

"I'm not drunk."

But we couldn't keep it up, and it was grossly unfair. When he saw that our magic box was making all that chimp noise, he just shook his head and laughed. He christened the tape recorder "soko-mutu ya nyumbani"—"chimps of the home"; and thereafter that was what we always called it.

With Manueri, chimp-watching took a new turn—for the better. No more the bleeding knuckles and frayed tempers of that awful first day; we now adjusted to the unhurried, silent, thoughtful manner in which a skilled man makes his way through the forest, looking always a little to left and right of the true path for any signs of space in the tangle ahead, even stopping occasionally and thrusting down the panga as a marker, before moving to the left and then the right in search of a clear way through. Having found which, a minimum of essential cutting usually got us across the most baffling array of forestry.

Our methods on finally approaching the chimpanzees became more cautious. At first, as on the first day, they got excited when they saw us. We had hopes that they might grow accustomed to our presence and, seeing that we did no harm, learn to ignore us. But in the event, unfortunately, just the opposite happened—more and more often, as the days went by, the response of chimps on spotting us was that they all quickly descended the trees, usually in silence, and made off deep into the forest along their own network of tracks which criss-crossed the undergrowth of the forest floor. Then we would have to sit down and waste a lot of time, listening for their next calls, which might be a mile or more off when they came.

The reasons, most probably, why we failed to habituate the chimps to our presence were as follows. For a start, there were always the three of us, and three people are quite obviously more frightening than one would have been. Secondly, in dense forest the chimpanzees must often have failed to see us distinctly at all, especially as, high up in the sunshine of the forest roof, their eyes must have had difficulty adjusting to the gloomy shadows of the forest floor; all the more suspicious, then, any strange creatures wandering stealthily below. But I believe both these reasons were less important than a third one—that we were seeing different chimps, or different combinations of chimps, on every occasion, so that in fact none of them had much chance to get to know us. Added to which, of course, humans are an extreme rarity inside the forest, so that their presence is bound to arouse suspicion or fear in animals, and the more so if the animals feel they are being actively pursued, and stared at with keen interest.

We soon gave up altogether the attempt to habituate a group of chimps to our presence—they were too mobile, too volatile; finding them was so hard and losing them so easy. We decided we must observe them without their knowing. An easy decision, but one which we never in eight months succeeded fully in putting into effect. For though the chimpanzees never seemed to be disturbed by the sounds of our approach, we found we had to deal with uncanny eyesight.

Our binoculars were a problem. We had to use them, as we were generally observing the chimpanzees from about sixty or so yards away. This distance, we found, combined several advantages. Further away, too many branches and leaves intervened and we simply could not see up into the tree-tops where the chimpanzees were. At sixty yards, the angle from our position to the top canopy was such that, by finding gaps in the lower canopies to peer through, we kept fairly well hidden and yet got a good, sideways on, view of the chimps. Coming closer to them increased the danger that we would be seen, and meant that we had to crane our necks in awkward angles in order to see anything.

But although we hid as carefully as we could, our binocular lenses must have glinted in shafts of light, and so the inevitable happened, sooner or later—one suddenly had the awful knowledge that a chimp was looking straight back down one's binoculars into one's eyes, a stomach-turning reversal of the field-worker's intentions. And then, with this knowledge, one just had to edge fractionally to one side, behind the cover of tree or bush, gently, and feign total non-existence for a few minutes, hoping for the best. "Moja naona mimi," I would whisper to Manueri on these tense occasions—"One has seen me," and we would all wait with bated breath for any tell-tale signs of panic in the trees ahead—worried moans, or shrill alarm barks, or the noise of foliage shaking as a party of chimps made their getaway, and perhaps the thud of feet as they jumped to the ground.

For this problem we found no solution: it was their wits against ours. For days we tried perfecting our camouflage (for our bodies were covered in jungle-coloured clothes) by covering our heads and binoculars and hands all over in camouflage netting as we got near the chimpanzees, but it was no use—the net over the lenses made the chimps look fuzzy and strained our eyes, and our head-nets kept catching on overhanging spikes and twigs, causing swearings and mutterings to break out on the forest floor and general bad humour to overtake the party. Added to which the nets were so effective that we kept losing each other, and had to take them off before we could spot each other again.

But, imperceptibly, we were improving. Manueri was showing us forest-lore and we were slowly cutting out inessentials and noticing the important things—we were becoming "of the forest." And one of our first major discoveries took place—wherever we tracked down a party of chimps, we discovered them eating a juicy yellow fig, which Manueri called "mukunyu" (later identified from our collected samples as *Ficus mucuso*). It was, for the chimps, the mukunyu season.

This fruit was obviously a great favourite with them. Day after day we found large groups, fifteen or more chimpanzees, gathered on the fig-trees, hooting and shouting loud and long as they stuffed great quantities of the figs into their mouths, chewed them up, two or three at a time, and swallowed them down into stomachs which already were full to bursting, looking around the while for another nice little cluster with the pink blush of ripeness on the orange skins. After a few hours of fig-feasting their feces were almost pure wads of indigestible fig-seeds and the smell under the tree, where millions of minute midges hummed over the débris, reminded one of nothing more than Paris pissoirs. During this fig season we got to know the location of a good many individual trees and the best approach to adopt in each case to avoid being seen, and the best place to watch from. We found that they were usually in sunny spots, often on the slope of a valley; and we came to admire these fine trees, which are extremely large and beautiful with an incredibly smooth sandy-brown bark contrasting nicely with the bright green of the leaves and the yellow fruits. We were as delighted as the chimps by the sight of a tree with "chakula *mingi* sana!" as Manueri put it, waving his hand downwards, wide-eyed, smiling—"*very* much food!" We grew used to settling down for several hours of continuous observation, identifying individuals as they moved about the tree, taking copious notes, tape-recording from close to the incredible din of their voices. In short we were thoroughly spoilt, and when in late April the season ended, and one by one the remaining fig-trees gave up their bounty to the chimpanzees and were "kwisha" (finished), not only were the chimps forced to change their tactics in order to find new sources of food, but we were left helpless and without any idea where to look.

During early May the shouting and the hooting, which had been our magnet and the essential signal we needed to get a compass bearing on and track down our target, all this sound and fury which we had come to take for granted, died away to nothing. It was as if every chimpanzee had left the area; to test this idea we went far beyond our previous study area but to no avail. All was silent. Day after day we wandered in the forest, trying one area after another, hearing what seemed to be a weak call, following it as fast as we could, getting hot and tired and ill-tempered, before finally, after hearing no more and finding nothing, we gave up. Several ideas went through our heads during those frustrating days and weeks, the most worrying of which was that the chimps, having spotted us on a number of occasions and fled, were now afraid and by mutual agreement, passed from chimp to chimp

1 mile

N

R. Bubwe

R. Sonso

R. Lwenti

Track A

Little
Kasenene
Hill

R. Lwenti

to
Butiaba

Busingiro
Hill

Siba Track

R. Siba

to Masindi →

● Much frequented fig trees

▢ Forest ▨ Bush

↗ Directions of most frequent
chimpanzee movements

Fig. 1. The area in which we made most of our chimpanzee observations is shown on the above map. At the time of the fig season we located chimpanzees feeding on large fig trees in the places marked. Arrows show the directions we saw the chimpanzees take when moving about the forest from tree to tree.

along the jungle telegraph, were keeping silent until we moved away from the forest.

Then one day we happened to be near some chimps and heard a few calls—individuals calling, no great group choruses of the kind we were used to—and came upon the chimps. To our surprise they were not up in the trees but down in the saplings just ten or twenty feet from the ground, two or three chimpanzees, rapidly stuffing something into their mouths and then, with great skill, moving outwards in the top of the sapling, bending it over by their weight, and finally leaping off it onto a neighbouring sapling. We looked carefully to see what they were eating: it was leaves, the young tender leaves at the extremities of the branches. We found feces, and they were green, almost entirely composed of leaves. I say "almost" advisedly, for it has never been shown that chimpanzees can survive on a diet of leaves and nothing but leaves; from what we saw we could conclude no more than that the chimpanzees, for periods of the day, were eating leaves: they may have been supplementing this with insects or fruit or pith, and we once saw them chewing wood. We now knew something of the conditions underlying the silence of the chimpanzees, which was as spectacular as their noisy outbursts had been, if more depressing.

As days went by we bumped into a few more groups, usually after painstaking tracking on a minimum of evidence, and found the same picture repeated time after time: small groups feeding voraciously on leaves as if they could never get enough, keeping quiet for most of the time. And in our wanderings we came to realise that there was no fruit on the trees, and none lying rotting under them: the figs had ended weeks ago and nothing had replaced them. Now the chimpanzees' behaviour made good sense: they had split up into little bands to forage all over the forest because there were no giant fruiting trees acting as focal points of attraction. And their silence could most simply be explained by the theory that leaves, in contrast to figs, were nothing to shout about.

Our idea that the chimps were keeping quiet because of our intrusion into the forest had been pure nonsense. We plodded on, day after day, sometimes drawing a blank, sometimes finding a little group.

And then, like all things, the lean times came to an end. It was nothing to do with the weather, not a dry season ending or anything like that; in fact, the dry season had coincided with the fig season and now there had been plenty of rain but no fruits. But the day came, in late May, when we heard once again the hollering and hooting of the good old days and came upon a sizeable group of chimpanzees in a small, rather gnarled understorey tree eating yellow-orange fruits which looked like a sort of Siamese-twin apricot, but unfortunately (for us) tasted bitter and astringent like nearly all chimpanzee foods. Again and again we found them on this species of tree, which was now coming into fruit all over the forest; it was called "ngrube" (*Melanodiscus* sp.). Conditions for watching were not too good because, as it was an understorey tree, our visibility was more restricted than when the chimps were high up above in the canopy. But that didn't matter: at last we were finding them easily again. For they now began to express their excitement as crowds of ten or more gathered on a bountiful tree. Whether it was the fruit or the company that made them yell we did not know. The trees were scattered widely, unlike the fig-trees, which generally had been separated from each other by no more than half a mile or so along a valley, or along the edges of a forest trace. So when a tree was finished we generally lost the chimps and were unable to follow them to the next tree, as we had sometimes succeeded in doing in the fig season. And we realised that the excitement caused now by the ngrube was less extreme than that caused by the figs: while a mukunyu would produce a jamboree, the result of a ripe ngrube was more like a vicarage

garden party. We got our observations, however, and although
at this time the animals tended to spot us and would then instantly flee, we were grateful for every small mercy after the
emptiness of the weeks before.

Looking back on our first months of observation, we saw
that we had witnessed three distinct periods in the chimpanzees' food cycle: the fig season, the lean season, and the ngrube
season. These "seasons" were determined by the forces gov-
erning the forest: the interrelations between its tree species,
the utilisation by each species of its own particular ecological
niche, each playing its part in the over-all pattern, each
struggling to survive against the relentless opposition of its
neighbours. So the cycle of the trees set the cycle of the chimpanzees. Besides this overwhelming fact, which, we came to
realise, was basic to an understanding of the whole of chimpanzee behaviour and social organisation, we had learnt a
great deal about their dietary habits. As well as the main
foods, we had collected a good many samples of species on
which they had fed once or twice. For instance, we had found
them eating a little red fruit which sticks jauntily out of the
ground at the bottom of a juicy green shrub called *Aframo-
mum*; it contains ginger and is eaten by the Africans themselves. And we had found another juicy shrub, with broader
leaves than the former, which the chimpanzees (and baboons
too, for that matter) broke off at the stem, peeled, and
chewed. This was *Marantochloa*. One day we had discovered
roundish balls made of woody fibres, the size of an apple; even
Manueri did not know what they were. Again and again we
found them under trees where chimpanzees had been feeding.
One day we thought of looking up, and there, all along a
branch, we saw a raw strip of inner wood where the bark had
been peeled off; its inside fibres had been chewed up by the
chimps before being spat out. Another plant was chewed and
spat out in this way, *Calamus*, the rattan of which chairs can
be made, the rattan which we hated, the rattan which barred

our way in swampy forest, when the going was tough enough without it, the rattan with needle-sharp spikes all along its stem where it nears the ground. It is an odd plant, for although it often creeps along near ground level and does not always climb, only the first few feet near the stem are spiked, and here the spikes are not protrusions from the pithy stem but are part of a jacket which can be peeled off. The chimpanzees, tough as their hands are, avoided the spiky bit and generally broke off a smooth length which they then sat down to chew, or they sometimes just chewed it where it grew. Sometimes they took a bit of rattan with them as they journeyed through the forest, just as the local Africans walk along gnawing at a length of sugar-cane. I once photographed a chimpanzee crossing the main road, and it was not until we studied it long afterwards that we spotted a food object, probably rattan, in the animal's hand.

We also tried some food experiments on the unsuspecting chimpanzees, placing fruits which do not occur naturally in the forest on trees and tracks where we knew they might pass, on their way to a fruiting tree. A bunch of ripe bananas was bitten into and individual bananas roughly torn off at the middle of the fruit; none of the bananas was picked off whole, and there was no evidence of peeling: this happened three days in succession. Mangoes left on the ground or put in trees were not touched and were left to rot. Of two avocado pears, one must have had a crack in the skin for the inside was picked clean by ants; the other was moved seventeen yards but we could not be certain what by—it might have been baboons, which almost certainly ate half a dozen maize cobs we left lying around, as we found their footprints and feces in the area. We also provided the chimpanzees with two unripe pawpaws (big fruits these, looking like a melon); one was totally ignored, and the other was left to ripen, then carried some fifty yards along a chimp track, peeled, and the inside eaten.

Later on, from our notebooks, we estimated that the chimpanzees here in Budongo spend six to eight hours of every twelve-hour equatorial day in the food quest, foraging or feeding. Ninety percent of the bulk of their diet is fruit, the rest being leaves, bark, pithy stems, and a small proportion of insects—mainly ants which they pick off the bark of the trees. How many pounds of fruit they eat each day we could not, of course, determine, but it must be a good number, for they are big animals (adult males weigh an average of 110 pounds, females 90 pounds). And the actual number of fruits that pass through their bodies, quite often stone and all, must be staggering, for the forest provides no fruits larger than an apple, and most are much smaller.

Their fruity diet probably supplies chimps with most of the moisture their bodies need, for we only once saw one drinking —up in the trees! It took me a while to work out what he was doing. He was dipping his hand into a hole of some sort and pulling it out and holding it above his head. I looked again and through the binoculars could see drops of water running off his hand onto his protruded lips. He had found a natural tree bowl full of rain-water a hundred feet up in the air. Oddly enough it was raining at the time but he didn't stick out his tongue to catch the drops, nor did I ever see a chimpanzee do this, or lick leaves after a shower. The hand-dipping technique was of interest, however, since this method of obtaining water was known to us to occur in the other three apes, the gibbon, the orang, and the gorilla, but had not, so far as we knew, been reported for the chimpanzee.

In their habits of excretion, chimpanzees, in common with all other known primates including untrained man, lacked most of the basic concepts so dear to some other kinds of animals such as cats: the concept of the lavatory, of hygiene, of choosing the moment with discretion, and covering your traces behind you. In short, during the daytime they urinated and defecated whenever and wherever they felt like it. And yet there were certain facts pointing to a sense of cleanliness, for we found that when chimpanzees defecated while walking along on the ground, they frequently found a fallen log to squat on; although we never actually saw this, we were forced to the conclusion by the fact that, of a random sample of feces which we examined, 30 percent were by the side of a fallen branch: a higher proportion than could be expected by chance. Was this a primitive toilet habit? It could be, for there is another well-known respect in which chimpanzees avoid contact with their feces: they do not soil their nests. This has often been reported by earlier observers who found perfectly clean chimp nests, and of the few I was able to examine (most being completely inaccessible) I only once found a little manure on the edge of one of them. We had observed the chimpanzees' early morning practice of defecating over the edge of the nest—a truly hygienic procedure. Here an interesting comparison with the gorilla was possible, for the gorilla invariably soils its nest. What was the reason for this difference? Later on we were to go south and see gorillas in their wild, mountain home, and only then was an answer to this intriguing question to come to mind. For the present, we just did not know.

One day we heard chimps calling from a new area where we had never been. There was a good reason for this but we didn't know it yet, and when we did find out it was something of a mixed blessing. The hooting we tracked down to a swamp, a horrible, prickly soggy swamp, covered with mosquitoes, frogs, and evil-looking puddles which, as we soon found out, were infested with a kind of worm which burrowed through the soles of our feet and produced blisters. What we discovered in the swamp was a tree of a kind we had not noticed until now—"igeria" Manueri called it—with masses of fruits looking like little green plums, and some indeed going slightly pinkish on the outside. These fruits were still unripe, but the chimpanzees had started selectively feeding on them and from their feces we could see how the ripe ones had been digested

1 mile

N

R. Bubwe

R. Sonso

Track A

Little
Kasenene
Hill

R. Lwenti

Busingiro
Hill

to
Butiaba

Siba Track

Sawmill Road

R. Siba

▣ Much frequented
patches of
Pseudospondias

☐ Forest ▨ Bush

↗ Directions of most
frequent chimpanzee movements

To Masindi →

Fig. 2. During the "igeria," or *Pseudospondias*, season, food was located in the areas shown above. The pattern of chimpanzee movements through the forest was now rather different from that during the fig season.

[1] A very old female sitting up in her nest.

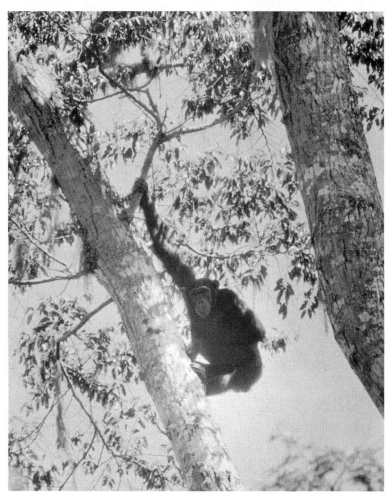

[2] As he watched us, this male was picking ants off the tree-trunk and eating them.

[3] Even on branches over one hundred feet high, chimpanzees rest their foreparts on their "knuckles."

[4] At the height of the fig season the Budongo Forest is a chimpanzees' Garden of Eden. This female tired of eating before she
had made much impression on the supply. The fig is *Ficus
capensis*.

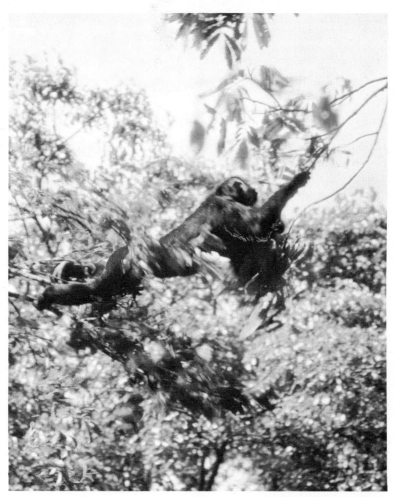

[5] One of the most spectacular forms of chimpanzee locomotion is swinging. The animal, here a big hundred-pound male, dives out, Tarzan-style, into space, catches a thin branch of the neighbouring tree, and pulls himself in to safety.

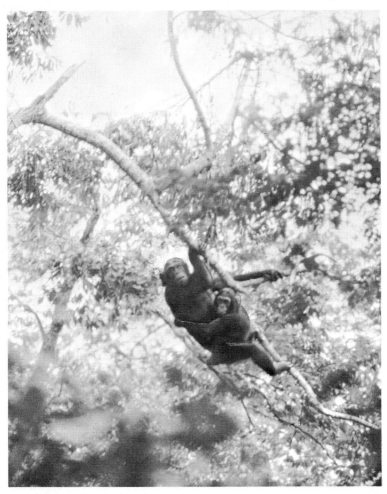

[6] When on the move, mothers often carry their young, even though, as in this case, the youngster may be several years old and well able to run on his own.

[7] A gruff old male stays behind as a sentinel to watch us after the other members of the group he was with have fled.

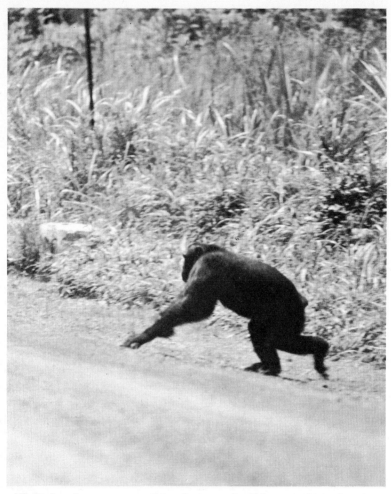

[8] Only when we saw this photograph did we realize that he was carrying an object, probably food, with him as he crossed the road which runs through the forest.

and only the stone remained, while the unripe ones had passed through the animals whole. I should explain that soko-mutu, unlike "mutu,"[3] does not spit out *all* the big stones he finds in his fruit; he eats faster and less fussily than we do, swallowing one here and one there as he goes and spitting out the rest. These fruits were over an inch long and the stones were three quarters of an inch long.

What we were seeing now heralded the beginning of a new season, the time of the igerias, and for us (happily we didn't know it) a month in the swamps, the only habitat where this species, the scientific name for which is *Pseudospondias microcarpa*, grows. So, from small beginnings, more and more igerias began to ripen, the fruits turned reddish and finally a deep dull purple, looking exactly like damsons. And did this mean jam for us? Jam out of those swamps? Hardly; these damsons smelled of turpentine and tasted awful.

This was a time for Wellington boots (incredibly, we had brought ours out from England with us, and we got some locally for Manueri) which, although invaluable in the swamps, were clumsy and caused us to fall a lot on our way through other sorts of forest to the swamps. This, too, was the time of the ants, which live in the swamps in teeming millions, criss-crossing high over the water on branches, and dropping down our necks as we brushed along. We were now in the Siba Forest for long stretches.[4] The swamps were richer there and more igerias grew, but, unfortunately, the Siba was the place of elephants and buffaloes. More than once Manueri refused to go on and, after an hour's sweating away through the thickets, with chimps calling temptingly close ahead, we would all stand around a heavy round footprint or pile of fresh

[3] "Mutu" is Swahili for "man." "Soko-mutu" (chimpanzee) may possibly mean "man of the woods." Or, using another derivation, it may mean "the man with the ugly face which should not be."

[4] Siba is the name locally given to that part of the Budongo Forest which lies southwest of the main road.

dung while Manueri examined it and said, with a shake of the head "Hi sasa"—"This is now"; he didn't want to believe it and we didn't want to believe it but we all knew it was true and shook our heads a few times and left it at that. For we had been warned about elephants by people who ought to know, and were prepared on this weighty matter to take their advice. Here there was no question of trial and error—our continued existence in this forest depended on our accepting the warnings of those who had gone before. It wasn't so much that either elephants or buffaloes were malicious beasts—no normal healthy beast is malicious to man unless provoked. The danger was entirely that we might walk silently into the middle of a herd, without either our or their knowing it, and be noticed by one animal which would sound the alarm and charge off into the trees, followed instantly and before we had time to think by all the rest of the herd, one of whom might run straight into us in the mad dash to escape.

We came to regard some parts of the Siba as hopelessly elephant-ridden; we left the chimpanzees alone there. Other areas further afield were elephant-free and we now worked in these. We watched chimpanzees arrive daily in twos and threes and fours, and found that they too disliked the swamp-water, for their tracks twisted and turned, following along fallen tree-trunks and any other dry spots, circling around the edge of shallow pools and crossing streams by tree-bridges where they did not leap across. We plotted their movements from the Budongo and up from other parts of the Siba and saw them pile into a couple of swamp valleys where the fruit was super-abundant; the noise output steadily grew. They fed and fed, the stones they spat out and their feces splashed down into the water below. Some parts of the swamp were drier than others and quite tolerable; we kept to these whenever possible. We saw the pattern of comings and goings we were getting to know so well, and during this period we hit on a new technique, which was to pay big dividends later on. We discovered it by accident. One day we were driving home after work when a chimp crossed the road just ahead. I slammed on the brakes and pulled up, and in the next fifteen minutes twenty-seven chimpanzees crossed the road just ahead of us. We identified each one by its sex and size and any other prominent characteristics, my eyes glued to the road while Frankie, beside me on the front seat, frantically tried to get the information down:

"One big male pink ears scar on left leg one mother with 'toto' [baby] quarter-sized one female in half estrus . . . pause . . . one old male grey back two three-quarters . . ." and so on. The tension mounted as they approached and we heard hooting and drumming close by. Then there was silence but for my commentary as they burst into view a few yards ahead and walked sedately or scrambled across the road. Manueri was delighted: "Kuanini sisi nakwenda kibrani?" he said— "Why do we go into the forest? We ought to stay on the road!" I chuckled at this thinly disguised plea for easier working conditions, but could not help feeling there was something in what he said. We had got information of a new kind. But it was a fluke: if we stayed on the road all day long we might not see a thing, chimps might not cross that day. It was a quick jump to the question "When would they be likely to cross?" but as yet we had no answer to that one.

So Manueri didn't get his way just then, but he had planted a seed which would grow. We went on jungle-bashing as before, saw the number of chimpanzees in our area level off and stay steady for weeks, and calculated that we had something like seventy or so chimps in our swampy valleys.

Besides our hard-won information on chimpanzee movements around the forest, we had during these first months made many day-to-day observations of the ordinary life of chimpanzees. This put us in a position, quite early on, to provide a few answers to the most commonly asked questions about this ape, based on our own experience.

For example, one question which is often asked is: do chimpanzees live on the ground or in trees? Early reports of their being seen in the trees were often illustrated by woodcuts of a hairy man-like creature standing upright on terra firma with a stick in his hand. In fact there is no "either or" about it: chimpanzees live both in the trees and on the ground, are equally adapted to both forms of existence. The amount of time they spend in the trees or on the ground is dependent on such factors as the time of day, and where food is to be found. In the Budongo Forest, the chimpanzees spent roughly 50 to 75 percent of the daylight hours in the trees; at night they slept aloft, and so it could be said that they were somewhat more arboreal than terrestrial. In this respect chimpanzees fall between the more terrestrial gorilla and the almost wholly arboreal orang-utan.

The fact that their food was mostly located in the canopy, and that they spent so much of the day feeding, helps to account for most of the time they spent in the trees. But they also spent long periods up aloft grooming each other, or looking out over the forest or, if they were youngsters, playing tag and other games. Sometimes, when food was fairly concentrated in an area, they moved from tree to tree by an arboreal route, each chimpanzee following the one before at a safe distance, making exactly the same limb movements as they swung between the trees, on branches which looked to us precariously thin. More often, when a move was being made to a new tree, they descended and followed one of their own chimp tracks to a new feeding place. Thus it largely depended on the distance to be covered.

A good test of whether an animal is arboreal or terrestrial is to see how it flees when really scared. If we stumbled on chimpanzees, they sometimes panicked, hurling themselves down from branch to branch in great thirty-foot leaps, quickly losing height, crashing to earth at a distance, and galloping off along the ground. This puts them with the forest baboons, as against the monkeys which invariably flee at tree-top level. Perhaps chimpanzees *are* more at ease on the ground: how can one tell? But the fact remains that ours spent more time in the trees and were superbly agile and confident climbers, thinking nothing of walking out along a thin branch and hanging above a 150-foot drop by one hand, while they plucked fruit with the other. Their aim too, when they swung from branch to branch, flying through the air for ten or twenty feet, was unerring. Not that they *never* missed, however; we twice saw chimpanzees fall. The first time was the most spectacular: having suddenly spotted us, a big male ran out on a branch to leap, the branch broke, and down he came about seventy feet to land with a mighty crash in the under-growth. Manueri unfortunately chose this very moment to start complaining about the lateness of the hour and how his tummy was rumbling. It was in the early days and we didn't know much Swahili, and we never managed to make a proper search for the fallen chimp; however, he was not near the spot where he fell, and I suspect he was not badly hurt. One thing struck us forcibly: in falling he held his arms and legs outwards and downwards, presenting the maximum air resistance and the best chance for catching any branches as he dropped; there was no tumbling in his fall. This falling-posture could be genetically determined, like the falling-posture of cats, although our evidence alone is insufficient to prove it.

The chimpanzees had a phenomenal ability to shin up branchless tree-trunks and a very special means of doing so. Their arms are longer than their legs as in all the apes, their hands are long by human standards, and we watched how they climbed upwards by using the arms and long hands to grasp somewhat around and behind the tree-trunk, moving each hand up alternately, while the legs provided the upward thrust, the feet being placed on the side of the tree nearest the chimpanzee, small toes one side, big toe the other. This method of climbing is extremely difficult for us humans because our legs are longer than our arms; nevertheless, it is not impossible, and certain Pygmy tribes have mastered the art.

Occasionally we saw a totally different way of moving in the trees, known as "brachiation"; this is really the gibbon's form of locomotion but chimpanzees can do it as well. With hands clinging to a branch above the head and feet dangling, the body is swung forwards, backwards, and to each side in turn, while the arms move forward alternately. This again is almost impossible for untrained humans, whose arms just will not take the strain.

On the ground or on stout branches the chimpanzees usually walked or ran quadrupedally, the weight of the fore-part of the body being supported on the knuckles (even high up in trees) while the hind feet were placed flat on the ground. When they ran rapidly on the ground their arms became strangely "divorced" from their legs, for while the latter moved forward alternately, the arms were swung forward together. Their manner of leaping over ditches at the roadside was extraordinary—flinging themselves forward with arms extended above their heads, they swung their legs forward under the body and landed feet first and fully upright, then swung the forepart of the body down and trotted off. Why they should adopt this complicated procedure is difficult to explain, but I suspect that the fingers and hands are too weak to take the full impact of the body as it lands and so the ape prefers to land feet first.

The most controversial kind of walk of the chimpanzee when on the ground is the bipedal walk, controversial because, being so reminiscent of human walking, it excited early travellers to exaggerate the frequency with which it occurs, producing any number of tales of little black hairy men who walk like people. In fact, bipedal walking is rather uncommon—certainly less common than just standing upright to get a better view. When it does occur, it seems to present no special balancing problems to the chimp, which, at first sight, is surprising. However, watching their movements in the trees, we noticed that they would often walk bipedally along stout branches, supporting themselves from above by holding onto other branches with their hands. Thus the upright body posture is frequently used by chimpanzees. As for the problem of balance, this long, loose-limbed creature scarcely seems aware that it exists. Nevertheless, upright walking does make the chimpanzees so fantastically like humans that one cannot help exclaiming. If they walked this way all the time no-one but a murderer would ever be able to shoot one. When they do get up it is either because their hands are full or because they want to look over an obstacle or get a better view, but this is not often; they are beasts, not men. Perhaps the nicest comment on bipedal walking was the one we heard in our earliest days, from Xavier, our tracker in the Bugoma Forest. He told us "it normally walks on two legs, but when seen by humans it walks on all four. When you first see them on the ground, they are standing on their hind legs, but they then move off on all four. It *pretends* to move like any other animal."

CHAPTER THREE

The Forest

In the heart of the forest it is quiet most of the time. It is as if every leaf of every surrounding tree is breathing slowly in the moist air, tasting its fragrance. Thin shafts of sunlight fall criss-crossing between the gently rising tree-trunks, and scarlet butterflies move noiselessly from leaf to sunny leaf. One lands on my arm, uncurls its tongue, and tastes the sweat. Some tree-trunks are gigantic, some are small; some round and smooth, others gnarled and coarse; some rotting and ready to drop. It is living so intensely, this forest, that I dare not breathe loudly or give sign of my animal restlessness. Every single tree tells the same tale, of steady, intense growth, no change of view, no desire for improvement, nothing but the calling of the wind high overhead and the answering tap-tap of branches and groaning of boughs. The tree's power is in its absolute steadiness and reliability; I feel vague and shallow by comparison. Yet the tree is stupid and I could cut it down. It has no vain desires, but neither has it any feeling: it accepts death without even knowing it is being killed. Yet I could not cut down the whole forest, the combined strength of all these trees is greater than mine. And I do not want to cut down, or even cut into, a single tree, I just want to feel the huge leth-argy with which it grows, the glory of its giant crown, and the

final inevitable twisted agony of its death. Every few days I
hear a giant crash, and I can tell the distance by whether it is
like a cannon or just a dull thud, and whether the ground
trembles. That a huge tree, so many tons of timber, which
has struggled towards the light, grown broad and spread its
branches wide against its neighbours, fruited season after season and fed hundreds of generations of birds and monkeys,
drained the soil of its goodness and enriched it with decaying
leaves, given shade and fodder to elephants, and provided life
for a million insects, that this piece of the structure of the
living earth should crash down with unbelievable destruction
from its firm unshakeable vertical is an event of such enormity
and yet such insignificance that I cannot comprehend it, any
more than if I witness the death of a fellow human being
whom I do not know. Some trees do not fall cleanly, but hang
as if reluctant to go, supported by lianas binding them to the
forest roof, suspended for a while to rot piecemeal high in the
the air. Others fall so terribly that they take two or three
neighbours with them—young trees of promise but without
firm roots. Still others find a purpose in death, forming
bridges over streams or gulleys, which will quickly be discovered by the civets and porcupines and chimpanzees.

So, day in day out, as in the population of a giant city, death
follows death in a fine random procession. No-one notices
these deaths except me—I notice a few. And I see, too, how
the saplings and shrubs and lianas and flowers and grasses all
rush to close the hole that has been torn in the fabric of the
forest roof; species struggles against species, each staking its
claim and straining to reach the light pouring in from above.
It is a struggle to the death, for only one can finally win, and
in the meantime I watch the fungus and beetles and ants begin the task of clearing away the previous occupant, which
lies now in a position that will never change, growing softer
and blacker in an ever-darkening tomb.

Other adventurers have been impressed by the forest. One, writing at the beginning of our century, described his reactions as follows:

For a whole day we crept through the skirts of the Hoima forest, amid an exuberance of vegetation which is scarcely describable. I had travelled through tropical forests in Cuba and India, and had often before admired their enchanting, yet sinister, luxuriance. But the forests of Uganda, for magnificence, for variety of form and colour, for profusion of brilliant life—plant, bird, insect, reptile, beast—for the vast scale and awful fecundity of the natural processes that are beheld at work, eclipsed, and indeed effaced, all previous impressions. One becomes, not without a secret sense of aversion, the spectator of an intense convulsion of life and death. Reproduction and decay are locked struggling in infinite embraces. In this glittering Equatorial slum huge trees jostle one another for room to live; slender growths stretch upwards—as it seems in agony—towards sunlight and life. The soil bursts with irrepressible vegetations. Every victor, trampling on the rotting mould of exterminated antagonists, soars aloft only to encounter another host of aerial rivals, to be burdened with masses of parasitic foliage, smothered in the glorious blossoms of creepers, laced and bound and interwoven with interminable tangles of vines and trailers. Birds are as bright as butterflies; butterflies are as big as birds. The air hums with flying creatures; the earth crawls beneath your foot.

Thus wrote Winston Spencer Churchill of Budongo, in 1908.* Before him, in 1890, the great explorer Stanley had recalled his experiences in the Congo forest to our west:

* I am indebted to Neville Spearman & Holland Press, London, for permission to quote at length from Churchill's *My African Journey*.

I have imagined the forest in listening attitude, the leaves resting in fixed but expressive stillness, and the grey, solemn trees, eloquent of antiquity, a venerable brotherhood involved in silent contemplation. I marvel at the age of the giants, and that impression of durability and resistance which they give.

And in 1902, Harry Johnston, governor of Uganda and an excellent naturalist, wrote:

I love almost more than anything else the forms of vegetation, the effects of sunlight streaming through many different tints of green, the gorgeous flowers on tropical trees, the black masses of mouldering wood, the gleaming white columns of aspiring trees, the emerald cascades of innumerable tiny leaflets, and the huge bold designs in individual leaves and fronds that can be measured in feet and yards; yet somehow or other I feel oppressed and disquieted in these African forests.

It is not for months that one comes to a deeper understanding of such a forest. Knowledge is the first requisite—wide knowledge of its vegetation types, how they influence each other and together compose the delicately balanced fabrics of the upper and lower canopies and the layers below, the shrubs and herbs. Alas, when we started work, we knew nothing about trees beyond a brief familiarity with the commoner English kinds, none of which occur in Budongo anyway.

First it was necessary to learn some of the species, but we were ignorant even of what characteristics to look for. Manueri was our source of information. "Miti gani?" we would ask him from time to time, as a particular tree caught our eye —"What kind of tree?" He would look the tree up and down, pick up a fallen leaf, slash at the bark with his panga to expose the inside colour of the bark and of the wood. Some trees exude latex at the slash, others have a distinctive smell, and he would put the bark to his nose. One species has both the appearance and the smell of raspberries and cream. Then he would reply, "Hi munyama," and we would note this down, together with a description of the tree's characteristics. Also, if it was a tree on which we had seen chimpanzees feeding, we collected a fallen sample of the leaves and, if possible, the fruit; in this the chimpanzees frequently helped us for, wasteful feeders as they are, they generally dropped a number of fresh samples for us to pick up. Subsequently these were identified by expert botanists and foresters. One thing we quickly learnt was that Manueri used the same name for several species of tree. "Nyakatoma," for instance, was used for two species of fig and one species which had a fruit with a stone in it. If pressed, he would explain that these were "nyakatoma number one, nyakatoma number two, and nyakatoma number three." All the nyakatomas had similarly shaped leaves (although far from identical) and all exuded white latex from the slash. The trees he really liked were the mahoganies, of which there were four species. These he would point out to us, with a note of approval in his voice, and would stand and gaze up knowingly at an immensely valuable tree. In all, twelve of the many forest species are really useful timbers, and felled regularly by the mill, while several others are potentially useful. Manueri knew all of these from his days at the mill. He also knew most of the others, but occasionally admitted he was stuck: he would try a few names but they would not satisfy him, the slash told him nothing, nor the smell, and the leaves were ordinary. "Hapana jua," he would say with a grin—"I don't know." On one occasion we had the good luck to be accompanied in the forest by a forest officer, Mike Philip, who told us there probably wasn't a man in existence who could tell every species in the forest at sight. He warned us not to accept Manueri's word blindly, but always take a sample to check on, and gave us valuable tips on species recognition—the shape of the buttresses, the way the branches left the trunk, the position of the tree—whether on a valley, or in a swamp.

As time went by we learnt that many of these solemn trees held secrets. High up on one, an orchid would be seen, nestling quietly in a crotch out of reach of our acquisitive hands. Another would have great outcrops of elephant's-ear fern along its branches—an epiphyte this, living on the tree but (unlike a parasite) not killing it. The larger epiphytes never ceased to amaze us—some species of figs, for instance, are epiphytic, and they grow so large that the result may appear to be a single tree with two different sorts of leaves, one sort belonging to the original tree and the other to the fig. Other figs become true stranglers: they begin life as an innocuous seedling, germinating on a branch high up in a healthy tree. Then they send their roots down the trunk to the ground, and the root system multiplies until it entirely surrounds the host tree, covering its trunk almost completely and killing it by sheer physical strangulation. In due course the host dies but cannot fall, being trapped inside the fig. It may rot away at the bottom, so that a hollow structure remains like a little cathedral; higher up bits of the original tree can be seen held in the fig's tenacious grip.

Such sights are the exception, however. Mostly each tree is just a single tree, larger or smaller, fighting its own slow insentient battle with its immediate neighbours for survival. And here begins what is perhaps the most fascinating part of the whole story. Different species have differing degrees of shade tolerance. Thus, while one species thrives in the conditions of prolonged sunlight at the forest edge, shooting ahead of all others, it falls behind another species deep inside the forest where it is forced to grow in almost perpetual shade. And so it is possible, from the species one sees around one, to tell how old the forest is in that particular area.

In 1947, W. J. Eggeling, then Conservator of Forests for Uganda, described in a brilliant scientific paper the natural

succession as it occurs in the Budongo Forest, where he lived
and worked for many years. Indeed, his first home was on the
very spot where we were now based, in a wooden house, for
our stone-walled bungalow had not yet been built. The excel-
lence of his work was something we only appreciated as time
went by and our understanding of the forest deepened. In
brief, he discovered that the forest was made up of a patchwork of four main forest types: woodland forest, *Maesopsis*

Fig. 3. Forest profile of *Maesopsis* forest. On this and the following two figures, the position, diameter, total height, and spread
of crown of each tree are drawn exactly to scale, but crowns are
not in fact as dense as shown. *Me* = *Maesopsis* trees. The remains
of two termite heaps can be seen.

forest, mixed forest, and ironwood forest, plus one minor
type: swamp forest. The youngest kinds of forest in Budongo
are woodland and *Maesopsis*, both classed as "colonising"
forest; these are replaced by mixed forest, and this in turn is
replaced by ironwood forest, which is the "climax" type, per-
petuating itself thereafter. This process of replacement is a
slow one, taking hundreds of years.

As Eggeling pointed out, the Budongo Forest is growing,
spreading outwards into the surrounding grasslands at a steady

rate of a few yards every year. On comparing earlier maps with
the forest as he found it, he noticed that in many areas grassland, now disused and heavily overgrown, had become colonising forest, and we had exactly the same experience when,
fifteen years later, we compared our maps with Eggeling's.

As a result of this constant expansion, the sequence colonising forest—mixed forest—ironwood forest can be seen, if we
choose the right spot, by walking inwards at right angles to
the forest edge. Firstly, we find ourselves in colonising forest
—either woodland, which consists of a variety of species and
occurs where the soil is poor, or, if the soil is richer, *Maesopsis*
forest. These *Maesopsis* trees are easily identifiable by their
umbrella-shaped crowns and their branches which jut out at
right angles to the trunk. This is the tree whose wood smells
of cold cooked chicken, and Manueri's word for it is "musisi."
Maesopsis is, in the jargon of the forester, one of the main
colonising species of Budongo. As we enter the forest we see
first small *Maesopsis* trees, then larger ones, some real giants
—and precious few other species. This is "kibirani toto"—
"child forest," and most of it is less than a hundred years old.
A century ago the area would have been covered with dense
elephant grass.

As we go in deeper, other species crop up with the *Maesopsis*: giant mahoganies, figs, barkcloth trees, and count-
less others which have no English names, and soon there is
not a musisi in sight anywhere—we are in mixed forest. What
has happened is that the *Maesopsis* which used to be here
have long ago grown to full maturity and died, being replaced
not by their own offspring, which, under their parents' shelter,
received too little sunlight to survive, but by the seeds of a
whole variety of other species, blown in or dropped in by birds
and animals, which were better suited to development in
shady conditions. This mixed type of forest is commoner than
any other type and is the most valuable economically, as well
as being the most variegated and interesting one, supporting

forty to fifty species of canopy trees and a great variety of wild life. It frequently changes its appearance, and may go on for miles, interspersed by streams and their valleys, patches of swamp forest, and even the occasional clearing, wholly natural, where for some reason no tree will grow. But slowly, as we go deeper still into the forest, the first ironwoods make their appearance, tall and slim, with their deep plank buttresses on which the chimpanzees drum. First one, then a

Fig. 4. Forest profile of mixed forest. This type of forest is characterised by a variety of tree species. *Ml* = *Mildbraediodendron excelsum*, *Ac* = *Alstonia congensis*, *Kh* = *Khaya anthotheca* (a mahogany). The remains of a termite heap are just discernible.

small group of them, until finally almost every big tree in sight is an ironwood (*Cynometra alexandri*). We are now in the oldest type of forest, the "kibirani kubwa" or "big forest," on ground which has supported nothing but trees for centuries. There is little herb and shrub life, it is as though these trees extracted every scrap of goodness from the soil. Clear a

patch of these trees and woodland or *Maesopsis* will grow
and the whole sequence must start again. There is little animal life on the ironwood-forest floor because, apart from the
annual fruits of the ironwoods and a few isolated shrubs,
nothing edible grows there. And yet, paradoxically, the fine
tracery of ironwood leaflets allows a good deal of light to fil-
ter through to the forest floor—more than in mixed forest.

Fig. 5. Forest profile of ironwood (*Cynometra*) forest. *Cyn =
Cynometra* trees. This is the oldest type of forest, and no old
termite heaps remain. This figure, and the two preceding ones,
were originally drawn by W. J. Eggeling, to whom grateful ac-
knowledgement is made.

Why then does so little grow beneath these domineering trees?
The reason is still imperfectly understood, but it is probable
that other species are unable to withstand the competition
of the ironwood's shallow but extensive and highly efficient
roots. Shade, at any rate, does not account for the failure of
other trees and shrubs to regenerate here.

It is fascinating to look at a map of the forest types and

speculate on the causes of their present-day distribution. Why is the whole forest not pure ironwood by now? Why do patches of *Maesopsis* occur deep inside it? In certain cases we know the answer, where areas have been cleared relatively recently in connection with timber extraction; in others we do not. Doubtless, small-scale clearing of the forest to make villages may have occurred in former times, but there is no actual evidence of this in the form of village ruins among the trees.

Soil samples taken inside the forest have, however, been found to contain traces of charcoal and pottery fragments, and it may be that some seven hundred years ago much of Budongo was grassland inhabited by Bahima cattle-grazers who, around that time, were migrating slowly southwards along the sides of the Rift Valley. Clear evidence of their passing has not been found in Budongo, but in the Bugoma Forest to the south there exists the remains of one of their kraals, now covered in trees. At that time, during the thirteenth century, Budongo may have been no more than a number of patches of forest standing where ironwood forest stands today; in the meantime these patches have grown outwards and joined together. This would mean that most of the forest is fairly young, for at present only some 32 percent is ironwood forest.

Additional evidence that much of the forest is young is provided by the termites. The tall mounds of grassland termites, often as high as a man, surround Budongo and are a very constant feature of open conditions throughout Bunyoro. These termites (*Macrotermes bellicosus*) cannot survive in forest. Eggeling described, and we too found, many disused, overgrown grassland-type termite mounds in the youngest forest types—woodland and *Maesopsis*. As *Maesopsis* gives way to mixed forest, the mounds become less prominent, being flattened, rather like tiny hillocks, as a result of the combined influence of rain- and leaf-fall. In ironwood forest there is no sign of the mounds of this species. If we knew the time it takes for a termite mound to change its shape from a tall, slim tower to a scarcely perceptible bump, we should have a rough chronometer for the forest.

But we do not know, and there are no records of any kind to help us. Even tree-rings, when they do occur, cannot be correlated with years in this land of perpetual summer. So the questions of the age of the forest and the extent of human habitation remain open for further study. Only the most recent history is at all certain. The African sawmill employees say that until they arrived as immigrant labourers early this century the forest was shunned by man, and this is undoubtedly true.

Certainly there are no Pygmies in Budongo, although they live in the Congo nearby. Did they ever live in our forest? It is impossible to know. There are not even any traditions, for the populations of Bunyoro have moved about, of their own free will and under pressure from the British government, which in 1912 declared the area north and north-west of Budongo an uninhabitable zone on account of sleeping sickness, and moved the entire population elsewhere. Thus while the patchwork quilt of forest types mirrors the forces which have been working on the forest for centuries, there is no certain way of telling which of these pressures were natural and which man-made.

The Budongo Forest is rainforest, it is tropical rainforest, and it is semi-evergreen tropical rainforest. What is the meaning of "semi-evergreen"? In England we use the word "evergreen" for conifers, for species which do not shed all their leaves in winter; those which do not we call "deciduous." In Budongo there are neither conifers nor winter, nor any situation resembling the one we are used to in the temperate zone. The leaves of all species are not shed at one time throughout the forest; each species has its own habits, and the forest as a whole always looks green. This makes it "semi-evergreen" in contrast with true evergreen forest, such as the fir forests of Scandinavia, in which the individual trees never shed all their leaves at once, and true deciduous forests in which, as in English woodland, winter sees every tree stripped of its greenery.

In Budongo the process of shedding is amazingly rapid. In many species, such as the mukunyu fig, there is less than one week between the time the leaves drop from their twigs and the time their tender replacements sprout forth; sometimes the old leaves seem to be pushed out by the new ones. The time of year when this occurs is very variable. Other species have more familiar habits—"muvule" (*Chlorophora excelsa*), for example, is truly deciduous, having a wholly leafless period from time to time. The most extraordinary species, however, are those in which some whole branches shed all their leaves at one time, while other branches may be all budding, and others still leafy. Such trees look raggedy brown-yellow-green all the year round and are an affront to the beautiful symmetry of their neighbours.

In its own complex way the forest is very much alive. The briefness of a human lifespan is such that we can scarcely observe more than the growth of a single tree, but studies such as those of Eggeling have shown us that the life cycle of each tree is part of the cycle of the trees of other species, and the cycle of all species combined is the life cycle of the forest. In our lifetime the Budongo Forest will grow. Time was when it did not exist at all: time will be when not a tree remains.

Tropical rainstorms have often been described, but what is less well known is how a forest affects rain. It does not simply cause rain-bearing clouds moving over from beyond the forest to condense, but it actually seems to cause the initial formation of the clouds in a windless blue sky, filling the air with moisture until it is saturated and can hold no more, at which point the sky empties itself, pouring back onto the forest in minutes all the water it has absorbed during the preceding hours.

The afternoon rains are the most spectacular, and we watched the cycle with fascination from our hill. After a clear blue sky all morning, during which all the crispness of the air is sapped slowly away, and the clear calls of birds fade to a deadness in the droning sticky air, noon finds the forest shimmering with a layer of hot haze above the dark-green transpiring canopy. The sun is now directly overhead and temperatures are approaching their high-point for the day. The humidity is intensely oppressive at this time: sweat will not evaporate, and the morning clothes which are hanging out to dry retain their wetness despite the blazing sun. Lizards bask on the rocks in our garden, flowers stare out boldly on the trees, their scent trapped around them in the steady air. Only down in the cool forest below are animals on the move. Outside this is a time of rest.

At two o'clock white flecks appear out of nowhere in the sky, and at the same time, very gently, the air begins to move. Tiny puffs of white, high in the sky, ride along unnoticed unless you search for them. By three they are bigger and turning grey in the middle, suddenly one blots out the sun and every living thing takes note. They are moving overhead quite quickly now, from the north-east, and the pattern of their shadows moves over the tree-tops, which stand quiet and still. Slowly the sky loses its battle and clouds blot out the last fragments of blue, turning now from white to an unpleasant grey; down below the moving mass it is suddenly a trifle cooler but none the less humid. A first roll of thunder is heard, and the rest follows swiftly. The wind, as if it could no longer be contained in the upper air, falls to ground level and curls the tree-tops, menacing black clouds ride by just overhead with enormous speed, an evil yellow glow suffuses the clouds. And then a curtain, with ends blurred at either side but clear as a knife-edge along its lower rim, appears in the distance over the forest, moving closer at a leisurely pace, blotting out little hills here and there, then silhouetting a ridge as it reaches the valley beyond, before that ridge disappears and the next in front of it is silhouetted in turn. The curtain is light-grey, and as it nears our hill a faint hissing can be heard above the sound of the wind; this is followed by the rat-a-tat of the first few drops on our corrugated-iron roof; the cats go indoors, doors bang, thunder peals and crashes overhead, lightning shows in brief gold streaks against the black forest sky, our skin turns to goose-pimples in the cold and as the curtain passes overhead the stampede of rain on the roof forces us to shout to make ourselves heard. We are shut in now, a little unit of people against an African force. Wind lashes the rain and I see the forest outriders, great trees and thinner ones, swaying jerkily and out of time. Unabated the drumming overhead goes on, as if the water were trying to batter the place down. The whole air smells deliciously of rain; I sit with a mug of tea on our verandah, perfectly dry, smelling this gigantic torrent three yards in front of me. It is the same feeling the triumphal march in *Aïda* has on the people in the front row. And like the great music of *Aïda*, it has to end, and the end is not a final brilliant overwhelming smash, but a dying off, a sighing regret. The sun quickly comes out, and as anywhere else after the rain, the colours are brighter, the air is fresher, and the birds begin to sing.

But the forest is cold after the storm, and each of its millions of leaves is coated with a film of water. As the sun breaks through and the air above the trees grows slowly warm, white vapour forms in the tree-tops and drifts idly upwards to the clouds; the forest looks as if a thousand camp-fires were smouldering below the trees. This is the rising mist which comes after the rain, and which has led to reports of "steaming forests" in travellers' tales. It is true that the forest steams, but the steam rises from tree-top level, not from the ground.

Inside the forest the air is clear and cold after rain, and a million raindrops fall from the leaves above; looking up, you see the tree-tops enveloped in swirling mist. It is only from outside the forest that the vertical shafts of mist can be seen, rising towards the clouds. This rising mist is quite separate from the mist of early morning, which lies in long banks along the valleys and over the sea of leaves, looking at times like a mantle of snow. This is a true ground mist, here elevated by the trees to 150 feet, which occurs on cloudy mornings and is gone by the time the sun has climbed half its way to the top dead centre of the sky.

Rain fell on 70 percent of our days at Budongo; on about half of these occasions it was really heavy. Sometimes we were able to watch it from the verandah at Busingiro as I have described, but most often we were down inside the forest itself. "Mvua!"—"Rain!" was Manueri's simple and meaningful remark when he detected the first signs. "Mvua?" we would invariably reply, looking up at the cloudy sky. "'Pana sikia?"—"Can't you hear?" We strained our ears and heard, faintly above the bustle of the leaves, the distant hiss of that rain curtain.

These storms were always a messy business. We had plastic macs but they were torn from the start and after nine months made little difference. At first Manueri had no protection, but we bought him a mac, for although he huddled under a tree-trunk, small and motionless, during the storms, as he had done for years, it was unfair to expect him to head for anywhere except home after it had stopped, especially because of the demoralising effects of the "second rain"—the dripping of leaves and showers from saplings that we knocked as we walked along after the storm was over. This second rain soon soaked his shirt and shorts and made him shake his head sorrowfully about his rotten luck. He looked askance at the green plastic coat the first time we gave it to him, then grinned and put it on. It even had a hood. Out of habit he squatted down as the rain hit us, and tore a huge gash in it. Then he discovered, as we had done, that if you squat down in a plastic mac, or adopt any position other than the vertical, water collects in the folds and spills into the inside through the gaps at the front between the buttons. Further, as we also knew, it is almost impossible to stop water getting in at the neckline. Still worse, one tends to heat up and get itchy if the coat is well and truly sealed against the elements. And then if, in order to protect the ears, one covers them in plastic, there is a constant humming and crackling sound and one cannot hear anything else. Looking back, I doubt whether Manueri was any more impressed with this latest triumph of civilised man than we were. As time wore on and little was left of his coat except the pockets and a few tatters of plastic held together by the seams, "putting it on" became more of a ritual than anything; perhaps he wanted to show us that he had not lost it, or perhaps he wanted a new one. But we could not afford new ones for him or ourselves and as they fell to bits we simply got wetter and wetter. Towards the end we did not take them at all but sat during the rain just like chimpanzees, knees bent, arms folded over knees and head resting on arms. In this way only our backs got wet through.

The worst thing to do, as we discovered one day, was to keep moving. We had been heading for the road where we had left the Land Rover, when the storm broke. It was a toss-up: whether to shelter or press on. We none of us knew quite how far it was to the road, all we knew was the direction. It was tempting to think the road was near, just beyond the furthest trees we could see. We pretended to recognise trees. In five minutes we were wet through; it was a heavy storm, great trees were creaking between the thunderbolts, threatening to hurl down branches and crush us in an instant. Manueri had seen this happen and he truly feared falling trees. We pressed on, our wet clothes filling up with water, our binoculars filling up with water, our camera getting wet, our shoes slipping in the mud, our glasses misting over. We tripped on unseen lianas and fell into the mud. It was too late now to do anything but go on. The rain was cold on our bodies and we shivered convulsively. Images of the dry comfort of home tantalised us: where was the road? Unbelievably, we cut through a patch of undergrowth and there it was, the red gash of the road, the channels on each side aflood with swirling water. Our legs felt heavy and the trousers clung; getting into the car we sat on sodden bottoms feeling miserable. Five yards were enough to tell me something was wrong with the car. I got out wearily, back into the teeming rain. We had a puncture in the rear tyre. The rain didn't matter any more somehow. Manueri got out to join me, and laughed as we jacked up the car: "Mimi mekanika, nataka shillingi"—"I am a mechanic, I want more pay." He helped mainly by just being there, a fellow sufferer, and the rain was not half so bad, or the frustration when the wheel nuts proved to be rusted on tight. Frankie sat in the car and shivered. When we got home, Semei, our camp guard and general factotum, laughed and asked if we had been swimming in the Sonso. We looked at him in his clean white shirt and khaki shorts, perfectly dry with his hair brushed, and felt strangely proud of the tough, comfortless way we lived out there, under the trees.

CHAPTER FOUR

Creatures of the Forest

In the Budongo Forest we slowly uncovered a secretive animal life of astonishing diversity. It might have been possible, by extensive reading, to have prepared ourselves for each discovery, so that we would have had nothing more to do than confirm our expectations, with a pompous "that's a such-and-such" and a self-congratulatory pat on the back each time a new species came our way. Instead, we entered the forest largely unprepared except for the bigger game.

For instance, we knew from game warden John Blower that there were many elephants and buffaloes in the Budongo, that leopards were common, and that there were plenty of deadly snakes, such as the Gaboon viper and the python. We also knew of the extremely shy forest duikers, the monkeys, and the wide variety of birds. And of course there were the chimpanzees.

But the forest had entirely its own way of disclosing what it chose to let us know. For the first month or so it told us nothing. We cut into it and hauled our unfit London limbs through it and occasionally watched the chimpanzees: this was, in the narrowest sense, our work and we concentrated all our efforts on it. At that time we had everything to learn, or perhaps not to learn but to re-learn. For it was faculties

we had had in our childhood and since lost which now were
of the utmost importance. We needed to use our eyes and
our ears and our noses, we needed to walk silently over the
twig-strewn forest floor, we needed the poise of flexed muscles
and agile limbs. And above all, we needed to learn the pace of
movement which is most suited to travelling through the
forest, a pace which varies from one forest type to another,
according to the number of obstacles and the usefulness of
animal tracks. We learnt from Manueri how to recognise
these tracks—how to tell the elephant's—wide and high—from
the buffalo's—narrow and high—and from the chimpanzee's—
narrow and low—and from antelope or pig tracks—intermittent. Along each track we learnt to read the two signs, dung
and prints, which each animal must leave wherever it goes.
Elephant droppings and buffalo-pats, chimpanzee droppings
and those of the duikers and bush-buck and pig—each has its
distinctive appearance, and gives a clue to the time since the
animal was last on the spot. This latter is an essential factor
in deciding whether to press on when elephants or buffalo
are about. The footprints add further information, telling us
which way the animal went: here again, this information is
of vital interest in the case of elephants and buffaloes.

From Manueri we absorbed the basic techniques of travelling and tracking in the forest, but he always knew and observed more than us, right up to the end. "Hi nini?"—"What
is that?" we would say to him, a hundred times a day, and
he always knew, even if he found it exasperating trying to tell
us. For instance, I remember a day in August, when we had
been wandering for six months in the forest and were beginning to feel confident, that we kept finding little heaps of
roundish balls of what appeared to be chewed-up fruit-remains
on the forest floor. "Hi nini?" I asked Manueri, to which he
replied with a gleam in his eye, as if he was sure I wouldn't
understand "Hi ndege"—"It is a bird." I could hardly follow
his description of the bird, but it seemed to be quite a big

one. Why then hadn't I ever seen one? I asked. Because, he proudly announced, they fly at night only. Now I thought I was on the track; it was some kind of owl, and I was finding the pellets. At home I checked my bird-books but found no fruit-eating owl. For more than a week we found the fruit-spittings every day—I gave up thinking about them. Then one day Manueri volunteered "Hi ndege sasa nyama"—"It is a bird like an animal." Of course! They were bats, fruit bats; Manueri was delighted that I knew. "Ah, mimi najua, mimi najua," I kept saying over and over again, "I know, I know," and then I began a quite lengthy attempt to explain how bats were not "birds like animals," but were true mammals, having no eggs but live young, while Manueri tolerantly listened to my painful Swahili, nodding his head seriously at the idea and secretly rejecting it. Manueri was like that: too old to change his views. He knew so much that was perfectly right and correct, the few mistakes he made were of no importance. His language, in this instance, distinguished "ndege"—the birds, things which fly—from "nyama"—animals, things which walk; it did not leave room for bats.

The forest is full of signs, if you can read them. We learnt the smell of civet, under trees where they are sleeping, and the look of the civet's "lavatory," for like cats they use a particular place or places to defecate. We learnt the smell where chimpanzees had been feeding. From English zoos we knew the smell of elephant droppings—it was just the same. We learnt to spot overturned leaves, which indicate that an animal has been past since the last fall of rain. We learnt to distinguish the alarm bark of the bush-buck from that of the baboon—the latter often having a slight intake of breath after the bark. We learnt to distinguish the twittering of the redtail monkey from that of the blue, and the totally different deep gargling roll of the black-and-white colobus. By ear we came to distinguish and know about a hundred kinds of bird-calls, but we could rarely identify them.

And slowly, diffidently, a little here and a little there, the forest began to disclose its secrets. For months we did not see any flower on the ground. Then walking into a glade, we found a beautiful russet bottlebrush plant standing all alone. Flowers are rare on the forest floor. Apart from the bottle-brush, there were pale-blue flowers like pansies hiding under leafy banks, tall slender mottled-green lilies, and lovely violet convolvulus bells which trailed among the bushes. Butter-flies, which emerged only during the heat of the day for a few hours either side of noon, provided another source of colour in the green-brown trees. The most striking is the kind which is crimson-winged; if you sit in a sunny spot one will generally come and settle nearby in the warmth. The older ones are raggedy and orange, like painted old women in Les Halles, but those in their prime have a pure redness which is the more striking for its green background. Higher up, bigger butter-flies move in the tree-tops, some a foot in wingspan, but these are rare. The real place to see butterflies is not in the forest itself but on the tracks through it. Here it is sunny and they course up and down all day, settling every now and then to look for food. And their preferred diet, the delicacy which renders them drunken, stupid with ecstasy? Dung, excrement, urine, all. We saw hundreds of them, twenty species at a time, clustered on small pieces of dung, side by side, jostling for position, and not letting outsiders in to join them. Swallow-tails, yellow or green with black dots, indigo-winged beauties which changed to a dull leaf-brown as they closed their wings —all bustled and gorged themselves together, the dainty guests at this, to us, sordid banquet. With our fingers we could gently pick them up; with a throw of the net we could catch them all; with one merciless blow from the tyre of our Land Rover we could wipe out every one.

J. H. Fabre, in his famous book about scarab beetles, has adequately described how we humans feel at this juxtaposi-tion of the beautiful and the beastly. Modern science has, of course, no time for such romanticising; it sees the biological world in terms of life cycles, the utilisation of food sources, and perpetuation of species. And, scientists or no, it is only the first time one notices that swallowtails feed on dung that one feels the incongruity. We accepted the fact quickly, the more so because dung, to us, became a source of information and so lost its repulsiveness.

Dung-beetles were also numerous in the forest. Attracted with incredible rapidity to any fresh manure, they arrived from all directions, crashing to earth by the food and burrowing into it. None of the ones we saw ever rolled dung-balls, however, as the sacred scarabs studied by Fabre did. Ours were either black or, more often, a shiny metallic green colour, and were mostly small except for one black giant which was two inches long. Within minutes fresh dung was alive with them, and within an hour or two it was gone. They fed inside the forest, in its cool depths, and not on the open tracks where the butterflies held sway.

Giant moths were another feature of our forest, although we only once saw one. We were sitting on the verandah of our home one evening when what I thought was a bat flew in and landed on the mesh door. Looking again, I could hardly believe my eyes: something was staring back at me—it was a moth with eyes as big as my own, sham eyes, vivid painted rings in the middle of its brown wings. An emperor moth, it was dazed and allowed me to measure it quite calmly: eight and a half inches from wingtip to wingtip! Too precious to risk its sudden death on the Tilley. We turned off the light and shook its perch and off it flew, back into the forest night.

Flies were abundant throughout the forest, some like our own house-flies but with brilliant red eyes. The largest, popularly known as "elephant-flies," were true giants (Africa has a giant of everything), black, white, and green in colour and an inch long. But of all the flies we met, the horse-flies made the deepest impression on us, mentally and physically. April

and May are their months, and I remember being warned of
them by a visiting forest officer earlier in the year. But somehow one never heeds a warning, and where there are snakes
and elephants and leopards, who could care about a fly? Suddenly they emerged, fully grown, and congregated on the foliage on each side of the forest tracks. At first there were tens,
then hundreds, and then thousands of them. And the most
amazing thing was that it was *movement* that attracted them.
Thus, walking up a forest track, we would be besieged by a
great swarm of them, but when we stopped and stood perfectly still they went away. And herein lay the great and awful paradox: whether to move and get home bitten, or stay
still and get nothing and nowhere at all. Most of the time we
ran, collecting flies in thousands; they clung to our clothes
and faces and hair. And being adapted for sucking the blood
of buffaloes and antelopes, they had no difficulty in penetrating our bush-jackets to the skin underneath. Each bite
hurt with a piercing momentary pain; automatically we swiped
and killed the flies which were slow to escape, but the swell-
ing and itching could not be avoided. They favoured our ankles and wrists and we wore bracelets of red bites which took
a week to subside. Fortunately neither of us reacted strongly
to them; some people have to be hospitalised after a number
of bites. I can see them in my mind's eye—long, thin flies, with
wings neatly folded over their backs, like English horse-flies
only slimmer—and I still hate them.

But there was an even deadlier enemy waiting for us in
the forest. An enemy which marches in a column of unimaginable length, and which, moving inexorably forwards, may
take a day and a night to pass a given spot; an enemy with organised military equipment in the form of soldiers with huge
jaws which clip shut and never reopen, even in death; an
enemy which consumes every living thing in its path that does
not escape before it is dragged down. Every portion is eaten
except the bones. I mean, of course, the safari ant. Suddenly,

plodding through the forest, Manueri (always up in front, poor fellow, and he knows it) shouts "Dudu!"—and we run, on, forwards, through them. We had, of course, to develop this technique; the first time we just stopped in the middle of them and gazed at the seething forest floor, while our legs slowly started going black as the ants crawled up us. That was the first time: the first time is always the most memorable and in this case it was the most painful. Having run out of the swarm, we strip off our bush-trousers and throw them aside, then pick furiously at those which got inside and have clipped themselves securely into our legs. The smaller workers come off easily but the big soldiers do not—we pull off their bodies and their heads remain firmly clipped on. It is fifteen minutes before we are on the move again.

And then there are the ticks. Fortunately, owing to our clothes, we are not unduly worried by these, but every now and then one manages to slip through. And ticks, bless them, have an uncanny knowledge of human anatomy, and always manage to find their way to a peculiarly intimate part of one's body, there, with one final heave, to embed their heads in the skin, clip on with pincer jaws which cause no pain, and proceed to suck themselves blue in the abdomen with one's blood. In the evening one finds them, while having an all-over wash. The question arises: how to get rid of them? All one can see is the blue-red abdominal blob and four legs on each side (for the tick, like the spider, has eight legs), so that the whole thing looks like an ugly flower with half its petals missing. It will not be pulled out. In our little booklet on tropical health we searched, the first time, for information. I had the tick and I felt affronted by the presence of this creature attached to me which I did not want. The book said that if we pulled the hind-end off the head might fester; the tick had to be persuaded to budge, all of its own accord. Two ways were suggested: by dousing it with paraffin, or by applying a burning cigarette end to its bottom. It did not mind the former, and I could not stand the latter. Result: on this and every other occasion we pulled the body off, leaving the head in. None ever festered, and one gave me a pleasurable itch to scratch for months afterwards.

The most surprising insect constructions we found were beautifully made chimneys, which occurred in clusters of a dozen or so around the base of trees, deep in the forest. Six inches high, they were perfect tubes of soil, brought up from below the leafy humus. They were made with extraordinary precision, a series of mud rings piled one on top of the other, perfectly round, about an inch in diameter at the base and tapering very slightly. We had no idea what creature it was that had made these; the chimneys we examined were always empty and there was nothing below them. Later we learned that these mud-tubes were probably made by emerging cicada nymphs. These nymphs lie underground, feeding on the sap of roots; in some circumstances, where surface conditions are unfavourable for their final metamorphosis, they construct these earthen chimneys and remain in them until ready for transformation into the adult insect: the buzzing, whirring, whizzing cicada we knew so well.

There were many other buzzing creatures, such as dragon-flies and beetles of all sorts, cicadas and lantern-flies and wasps, too many to describe them all. One extraordinary insect was the "buttress-fly" as we called it—a creature with a tiny body, long spindly legs, and fine wings, which lived only between the plank buttresses of giant trees—at least, that is the only place we ever came across them. When we first noticed them they were always moving up and down, slowly, drifting about in the dim space between the buttresses but, as we drew nearer and they detected us, the speed of their movement increased: they went up and down less far but much more rapidly, as if quivering with excitement.

But there was a kind of insect which had an even better technique for warning us off: believe it or not, it tried to intimidate us with *sound*. It generally happened like this. We would sit down, for lunch or to listen for chimps, and would become aware of a rhythmic rustling in the leaves close by, a sound which was just like the footfalls of some stalking animal, slow and regular. After a search we could find the cause —a large number of termite soldiers were beating with their heads among the leaves and beating in unison. If seriously disturbed they lost their rhythm but quickly picked it up again; if we kept still their whirr-whirr grew weaker until eventually the symphony stopped.

Termites, occasionally, swarm. This we found in no uncertain way when, waking up in the middle of the night, we discovered nasty squashy insects crawling all over us. A flash from the torch gave us some idea of what was happening; when the lamp was lit there was revealed a seething mass of little bodies crawling in at every crevice around our closed mesh windows and under the doors—millions of termites creeping in on us to share our warmth and our bed. There was nothing to do but retreat. We tried the next room, laying a paraffin barrier behind us, but it was no use. So we moved to the last room, barricaded the crevices and cracks with paraffin-soaked paper, systematically executed every "dudu" in the room, and finally dropped off into a light sleep, broken every half hour or so as one of these wretched insects wandered over our faces. It was a horrible night. In the morning we surveyed the carnage inside the house; outside the windows and doors was a canopy of silver wings, million upon million of them; we picked them up in handfuls and let them slip like silver snowflakes between our fingers, glinting in the morning sun. And their bodies being good to eat (Africans consider them a delicacy; we tried them fried with onions and they tasted like tiny shrimps) all the walls and corners of the house were covered with ants, spiders, wasps, and other carnivores of the insect world carrying the termites off to their food-stores for future consumption.

There was one beetle which was so magnificent that I must tell of him. He dropped to the ground beside us one day in the Siba Forest, scuttled under a leaf, and lay still. He had hit the ground with such a whack we were both startled, and when I uncovered him we saw what a beauty he was: brown and white and green and black, *Goliathus goliathus*, the goliath beetle, largest in the world. I picked him up, put him in our polythene lunch bag, popped it in a breast pocket, did up the button, and forgot about him, leaving further examination until we got home. I did not for a moment think that my victim would be uncomfortable in his new surroundings.

It was an hour or so later that I suddenly felt something on my neck. I put back my hand and felt this enormous hard insect. With wild infantile imaginings I let out a shriek and tore off my jacket, cricking my neck badly in the process. For once, I was scared out of my wits, for a second or two, and the whole episode is stamped irrevocably in my mind. The beetle came off with my tangled jacket: he was not in the least harmed, just looked at me as if surprised at his own power, making me feel ashamed. He had cut through the polythene and crept out of my pocket, scared me, and won my respect: I never once thought of harming him. I wanted to take him home for a photograph, but I also felt the need to know where he was at all times. I finally decided that both he and I would be quite safe if I kept him in my handkerchief, dangling from my hand.

Back at home I put him on the floor. He was slow and unable to walk well, his feet being specially adapted with twin claws for climbing vertical tree-trunks. Just as I was settling down to watch him, I got a surprise—he sprang with a whirr like a toy aeroplane up into the air, sailed once majestically round the house and then, straight as a die, headed off towards the Siba, one mile away, towards the exact position where I had picked him up. How he did it I do not know, but that beetle must have possessed a wonderful sense of navigation, as bees do.

Budongo has bees too. One day as we were walking home through the forest Manueri suddenly stopped and said, "Asali"—"Honey." His head was cocked on one side; we listened, and could faintly discern the hum of insects; following him we traced it to a fallen tree. There were three separate holes in the rotten trunk, and at each bees could be seen entering and leaving. It was a scoop—Manueri's face beamed with delight. Next Saturday he would return with fire. Poor bees!

We accompanied him to see how it was done. He picked a bunch of grasses outside the forest and had, as always, a box of matches. In addition we carried an empty ten-gallon oil drum for the honey: he assured us there would be lots of it. Fortunately the tree was not far inside the forest or we would never have found it, but there it still was, with the bees humming to and fro. Where did they find the flowers, I wondered, thinking of the dank brown-and-green forest floor we knew so well, where flowers are rare or non-existent. And I remembered the canopy where millions of tiny blossoms, visible only from above, appear on one tree or another all year round. That in turn tallied with the fact that bees were very rarely met with on the forest floor. Here they had come down to their nest, but as each bee left it flew upwards to the canopy again. Some bees probably never come down to ground level, for we had come across nests way up in the trunks of living trees—these, with a shrug, Manueri had always left behind and forgotten. Here, at last, was a nest on the forest floor: manna from heaven.

So under each hole he placed grass, and gathered sticks to catch fire from the grass, and lit the grass, which flared up merrily. We stood well back, having discovered that these little forest bees did not have a correspondingly mild sting. They had resented our presence near the nest; what would they now be like as their home caught fire around them? But it did not catch fire: the rotten wood simply smoked as the flames licked around it. Manueri stood by the tree cutting into it with his panga. Every now and then he pulled a bee off his neck or arms, but the stings did not seem to bother him much. Feeding the flames and cutting, he worked inwards towards the nest. Bees were now pouring out in their thousands and Manueri worked on among them unperturbed. Within minutes he had hold of the first honeycomb and shouted that it was "mzuri" (full of honey), and it went into the drum. Others followed in unimaginable quantities—if they were all full of honey I guessed we would have gallons of the stuff. The bees collected around the drum with its honey-smell and began to go into it; more and more bees kept coming in. Manueri now started a fire under the drum, for he said that unless the bees were killed they would eat all the honey. After an hour's work at the tree the last honeycomb had been removed and the drum was nearly full. It was hot now and the remaining live bees were suspicious, flying around and around but not going into the heat. Covering the drum with a jacket, we left the thing to cool down and went off home. I took the lead with the panga; Manueri's hands and arms were puffy and paralysed from the stings.

In the afternoon we returned with vessels for the honey and muslin to strain it through. Bees were still around in small numbers, which increased when we removed the jacket and the honey-smell escaped. We had to work fast. The scene inside the drum was hideous: about three solid feet of dead bees on top, then the wax of the honeycombs, congealed and formless, blackened from the soot of the fire, all of which was thrown away, and underneath the sooty golden honey, dotted about with bees and small lumps of wax. This we poured straight through the muslin into the bowls and pots we had brought. There was less than we had expected, about a gallon in fact.

The carnage of the bees had been appalling but we were

hungry for the honey; we saw that we had worked in cold blood and were not ashamed. Great was Manueri's delight and the delight of his friends and our delight when we ate the honey, that day and the next and for a couple of weeks thereafter.

The bird-life of the forest is heard rather than seen. My immediate memory is of a constant backcloth of song, harsh cries and softer tones weaving their way to us through the trees in a complex multidimensional pattern, for birds are not static, and so as one listens their voices move close or out of range, drowning others, or allowing them, like hidden substrates in a symphony, to dominate despite their timid tones. And all one sees is the trees, the leaves falling. One searches and searches for a bird, any bird, but sees nothing. And then, suddenly, a red or violet streak moves against the green and is lost again instantly.

It is not possible to make any generalisations about the birds in the forest. There are big birds and small ones, brilliantly coloured birds and dull brown ones, noisy birds whose voices carry half a mile and quiet ones whose faint babbling scarcely reaches the ground. Among the biggest is the giant black-and-white casqued hornbill, an extraordinary bird whose casque (the protuberance of horny substance on top of the bill) is a giant resonating chamber for its extremely unpleasant, harsh voice. A Uganda folk-tale relates how the hornbill came by its voice. Once upon a time the hornbill had quite a nice voice, but she was so vain about it, and was always trying to sing such high top notes, that her voice broke, and unfortunately all her children inherited it, and now they are forever telling the other birds and animals what a beautiful voice their mother once had, and how much it was admired, and all the jungle is tired of hearing about it.

At first sight the hornbill is an amusing creature, looking like an overgrown magpie. Because of the size of its head and bill it always looks top-heavy, and seen from below it has the shape of a cross, head and tail extending an equal length from the wings, which move up and down at perfect right angles to the line of the body. Generally it caw-caw-caws as it goes, and its wings make a rushing sound, not musical like a swan's or whistling like a duck's, but just plain flap-flap-flap as if the bird was making heavy weather of it. And with such an un-aerodynamic shape goes the splendid Latin name for this bird *Bycanistes subcylindricus*, which somehow manages to convey the Rube Goldberg quality of the whole job. I was prepared to see one break down at any moment, yet the things obviously didn't mind flying because they were to be seen winging their noisome way across the forest in ones and twos and threes at all times of the day. Whether the bird is ugly or not is a question each person decides for himself; my own view is that the closer you get the uglier it becomes, but seen at a distance against a backcloth of forest it makes an attractive picture.

Two types of black-and-white hornbill were present in the Budongo, one, the Uganda type, with a square-fronted casque and black central tailfeathers, the black reaching the tip of the tail, and the other the Congo type or white-thighed hornbill, with a pointed front to its casque and a white band across the end of the tail. The existence of these two distinct yet, broadly speaking, very similar types raises again the fascinating problem of the history of the Budongo Forest, how long it has been in existence, whether it is a remnant of a much wider forest, and at what points, if at all, it was once joined to its vast brother, the Congo rainforest which now lies to the west, beyond the Albert Rift. The answers to these questions are speculative and there is no agreement among scientists; if we could know more about the subject we might be able to plot the movements of animal species and show how different forms have emerged through isolation from one another. As it is, the existence of the two hornbill forms, sharing a single niche in this forest, tells us little more than the fact that long ago the ancestral black-and-white hornbills became split by an unknown geographical barrier, perhaps the great Rift Valley; that they remained apart and developed certain differences of casque shape and tail pattern, and that now, whether by migration of the hornbills or by movement of the forests themselves, the two types occur together in this locality.

Enough said about the hornbill, and yet it was the only bird which seemed to believe in self-advertisement rather than self-concealment. A big bird but much less often seen was the black-billed touraco, at once a brilliantly coloured bird and one which cannot be seen until it flies. The body and outsides of the wings are light olive green, and while feeding the bird moves about in the branches by rapid sinuous runs and jumps. The effect of this colour and speed is that the eye is unable to follow the bird and one simply does not see it. Perhaps if there were not always some movement of the leaves one would. But then, suddenly, it flies, and the unfolded wings shout their violent scarlet message; it was the most powerful colour impression the forest had to offer.

At the other extreme was a bigger bird, the crested guinea-fowl, which, despite its bright blue-and-red head, is beautifully camouflaged in a dark greeny-blue mantle of feathers, speckled with little blue-white spots. An elegant example of adaptive colouration this, for no colour-combination could be better for a bird which spends most of its time moving around the forest floor, among the deep shadows, the dark greens and blues and browns. Unlike its grey-coloured open-country cousin the tufted guinea-fowl, this forest bird keeps very quiet most of the time. Its call is so soft that it can only be heard when the fowl are very close, and it lacks entirely the harsh, carrying, rasping call which the bush-fowl makes as it settles to roost in the evening. During the first months of the year the fowl were in flocks in Budongo, and we would bump into twenty or thirty birds together. Later, in April, the flocks became scarcer and pairs were the rule, and then in May and June the pairs would be accompanied by their broods—anything up to ten little chicks trailing after their parents. As the young grew older they quickly came to look very like the adults but they had not yet learned caution, and sat about on branches they had flown up to, gazing at me as I stood below, gun in hand. But they were as yet no use for the pot—all bone and feather, very little flesh.

A noisier game bird was the local race of francolin, whose rasping call we often heard, especially at roosting time. This little African partridge is brown with white spots all over, and has a brilliant red beak and red legs; but it is much less numerous than the guinea-fowl. And lastly, once only I saw yet another species of red-legged fowl or partridge in the forest, which came pecking past me as I sat watching some chimpanzees. There were only two of them, and from the description I made of them I later identified them as Nahan's forest francolin, a shy and uncommon bird.

There were other brilliantly coloured birds, some with metallic hues, such as the broad-billed and blue-throated rollers and purple-headed glossy starlings; others were dull, like a violet bird[1] I watched one evening, as he sat deep in a valley on his white-soiled perch, flitting up to take a fly and landing again, flitting up again and landing, as the forest grew misty and cold.

But one's memories are mostly of sounds. There is the soft song of the blue-spotted wood dove which, starting on a high note, and repeating it a few times, lets it fall with increasing tempo and then, when it touches bottom, brings it up again, slowing the tempo as it does so, until it hits the first note again, which it repeats slowly a few times just as it did at the beginning of the phrase. To think that such a ca-

---

[1] *Melaenornis edolioides*, the so-called "black flycatcher."

dence, which might have inspired a romantic composer such as Dvořak or Ravel, is merely innate behaviour, an unthinking response! There was only one bird whose song was better, the white-browed robin-chat, which lived outside the forest and whose liquid tones came in phrases which began ever so quietly as if the bird was a long way off, then built up to a great crescendo of unbelievable intensity, which suddenly stopped. It was as if the bird were singing as it flew towards you, and yet I have watched the whole performance, which occurs at dawn and dusk, and seen the bird sitting perfectly still at the bottom of a bush, only its throat heaving as the music grows louder and louder. I do not want to deny the beauty of our nightingale's voice when I write about these African birds—for I believe the nightingale is a finer singer than either of them; the beauty of his song is in its unpredictability, whereas these other two repeat a sequence over and over again, and thus one inevitably tires of them in the end.

There was the yellow-bill, a close relative of the cuckoos, that laughed a shrill cackling laugh which mocked us as we cut our painful way through the swamps with rattan spikes tearing at our fingers and arms and pricking us teasingly through our clothes. There were four kinds of cuckoos; there were birds that boomed a single penetrating note; woodpeckers that tap-tapped at the trees above us; and a strange repeated note from a bird we never saw, sounding like a whip flying through the air and coming down with a crack. Manueri said this noise was produced by a squirrel, so perhaps it was not a bird after all. And there were the parrots. These were mostly grey parrots, though some were a green colour, and we rarely saw them by day. Yet they are daytime birds; indeed, in a Uganda folk-story, there is a ditty which mother parrots are said to teach their children before they leave the nest, exhorting them to keep an eye on the sun:

Never get up till the sun gets up
Or the mists will give you a cold.
And a parrot whose lungs have once been touched,
Will never live to be old.

Never eat plums that are not quite ripe,
For perhaps they will give you a pain;
And never dispute what a hornbill says
Or you'll never dispute again.

Never despise the power of speech;
Learn every word as it comes.
For this is the pride of the parrot race,
That they speak with a hundred tongues.

Never stay up when the sun goes down,
But sleep in your own home bed,
And if you've been good, as a parrot should,
You will dream that your tail is red.

The last line is explained in the accompanying story: it was
the parrots' ambition, at the time concerned, to get red tails—
an ambition they have since achieved. The line "Never stay
up when the sun goes down" seems indeed to be well taken
by every parrot. For they were most impressive in the evening
as they flew in parties, high overhead, to roost. I do not know
where they roosted—perhaps, like the hornbills, they left the
forest at night to sleep in the surrounding open ground. But
every evening they would fly over quite high, their pure calls,
interspersed with wheezy squawks, drifting down to us in the
forest below. Short, quick wingbeats they had as they sped by,
and the falling of their notes out of the violet gold-rimmed
sky had all the magic that is Africa. After them, the dragon-
flies appeared for their dusktime feed, a few moths and bats
emerged, and as the creatures of the day curled up and
crawled into their sleeping places, those of the night were
stirring and smelling the air and peeping out of half-open lids
at the encroaching night.

Then there is that strange cold-blooded half-world, as it always seems to me, of snakes and frogs and slugs and slimy things. One such was a kind of "snail-slug," neither one nor the other but a bit of each, which we frequently found on the broad-leaved shrubs of the forest floor. This creature was brown, an inch or so long, and looked like a slug with a hardened, flat, spiral-shaped disc on its back. It really did seem to be an intermediate stage between the slug and the snail—to be either a snail in the course of losing its shell, perhaps exchanging this form of protection for an unpleasant taste, as the slug has done, or to be a kind of slug in the course of evolving a true shell into which it would one day retreat; but this creature lacked the ability and even the tendency to contract its body under the shield when touched.

Tree frogs were common, mostly small, and they came in a wide variety of colours: one, for example, was an inch long, and handsomely turned out in leaf-green livery with spotless white knee-caps. Often as we walked along, small ground frogs leaped out of the way of our descending feet, missing death by inches. We rarely had a good view of one of these but once we did succeed in catching one and bringing it home. I cunningly arranged for it to leap, on its release, into the neck of an empty chianti bottle, then stood the bottle right way up and was satisfied to see that the creature could not escape. It was about the size of a penny, and khaki coloured. I wondered what it ate, and decided that the little ants, which were crawling in columns up the walls of our house, might be suitable for it, so I caught a dozen or so and released them in the bottle. Then I pushed in some grass and twigs and a bit of earth, and hoped Froggie would be happy. But he wasn't. He hung glumly upside down near the top of the bottle below the neck, disregarded ants which crawled under his nose, and leaped blindly against the bottle walls whenever he was disturbed. We could not keep him; his natural dignity was gone; we derived no pleasure from the spectacle of this now thoroughly dirty frog tumbling in the bottle. So we let him go.

Exactly the same happened with the tortoise. There were two little blue-shirted, khaki-trousered boys, the eldest of the huge family of Marco Okenyi, the local game guard who had at the very beginning introduced us to chimpanzees; he had moved house since and now lived just down the road.

These two boys went to school every day, and on their way they had taken to coming up to our house with a bucket, and in the bucket there was always something different, either tomatoes, or bananas, or maize, or avocados; but the price was always the same: seven cents. We generally bought the goods, and the boys walked away. They were always solemn; one only spoke, he looked at me as his father looked at elephants, and he took the little silver coin. They asked no questions and neither did we, but treated each other in a businesslike way.

One day there was a tortoise in the bucket. The boys did not seem surprised and the price was the same. "Natoka wapi?" I asked—"Where does it come from?" "Kibirani tu," the talking boy said, jerking his head slightly towards the forest. It was no use asking him to take it back; he would probably just let it die in the bucket. The boy's two deep eyes were burning into me without a doubt that I would take the prize. We looked around. There were boxes, the ones our food arrived in every week from Masindi. I picked up the tortoise, which was a land tortoise, clean and in fine shape, but he would not put out his head to look at me. He must have been newly caught. We gave him straw and paid off the boys; normal life resumed. But for Gogo, as we called him (after the Swahili for tortoise: "nyamagogoto"), life had taken a turn for the worse, and he was not a depressive tortoise who would sit with his head in and suffer: he fought back. Time after time he got his front legs on the side of the box, heaved himself up to the edge, then fell with a crash onto his back, where he lay until one of us put him the right way up again. We gave him water to drink but he stepped on the edge of the bowl every time and made a mess. And what, we wondered, does a land tortoise eat? After trying everything we had in the house and everything that grew in the garden, Frankie finally found that a mixed diet of tomatoes and bananas set him eating busily. We built him a brick-walled enclosure in a corner of our verandah, so that he could walk about. And we used to let him out when we were on the verandah, watching, to walk about and puzzle the cats. But Gogo remained unhappy: it was obvious. He still tried to scale the brick walls. One day he succeeded in pushing off a top brick and clambering through the gap. We found him at the edge of the garden, defeated by a steep slope: he had been heading straight towards the edge of the forest. After that he escaped again and again; he had huge resources of strength on the luxury diet we were feeding him, he could heave bricks around like a builder's mate. Gogo did not like our verandah and he did not want our hospitality. In addition, we had used him for an experiment with the chimpanzees, putting him in their path to see their reaction (there was none, incidentally; they just walked straight past him), and so we could not justify keeping him any longer. One day Manueri and I took him down to the edge of the forest and let him go. He wanted to snuffle about in the leafy depths and find his own suppers. He was sick of tomatoes and bananas; he made this clear to us, and we gave him his liberty.

A worse fate befell Sally. Sally was an olive house snake, eighteen inches long, with a silken skin and beady yellow-green eyes. She was friendly to humans, but death to geckos and lizards, which she caught, constricted, and ate whole without a flicker of emotion, two or three times a week. Sally was a gift to us from Janet Stoneman, a snake-handler in Masindi, who obtained snakes from local Africans and caught some of the deadliest ones herself, such as mambas, for an

agent in Nairobi who supplied zoos all over the world. There
was no great demand for Sally at that time however, and she
had been in Janet's care for long enough to be fully accustomed to crawling around on human beings and exploring
them intimately—all one had to do was relax and not make
any jerky movements which she might misinterpret. While on
the move, Sally lived in a little gauze bag, and at home we
put her in a big box with plenty of straw and a gauze top
attached around the edges with drawing pins. It was this
method of attachment, though I did not know it, which was
to prove our loss and her undoing.

For weeks she worked with us. Her role was a simple one,
and she did it splendidly. She had to lie on chimpanzee tracks,
preferably wriggling a little, so that we could observe the
chimpanzees' reactions to her, in order to see whether they
would instinctively fight shy of a live snake, or investigate
one, or even attack. In order to achieve this we were forced
to tether Sally to stop her slipping away, but we did so by a
completely painless method. A piece of sticky plaster was
wrapped round her tail, and to this a fine cotton thread was
attached, on the end of which was a stone too big for her to
move. (Gogo had been tethered in a similar way, but to a
much larger stone, since he was immensely strong.) As long
as Sally was in the shade she did not mind this. And we made
the perhaps significant discovery that no chimpanzee ever
came near the snake, although we were unable to prove that
any ever avoided her since we never saw them anywhere near
her! It is entirely possible, however, that their eyesight had
detected her at a distance and that they had then taken another route.

Sally lived with us and consumed our geckos for a month
or more, and during this month our two cats and four kittens
took to sleeping during the heat of the day on the gauze roof
of Sally's box, in a cool back-corner of our verandah. Unknown to us, the weight of the cats was slowly forcing the

gauze downwards, and where it was pinned at the edges it was tearing. One morning Sally was gone. We quickly found the cause, but we did not find Sally. We looked under every stone, we cut away the long grass. We felt she was nearby, as on previous occasions when she had escaped she had never gone far, usually hiding under a big fallen leaf or in a tuft of grass. But this time she had beaten us and we gave her up for lost. On the sixth morning after her escape a sorry sight greeted us on the verandah: Sally was distributed about the place in bits and pieces an inch or two long. She had been nearby all the time, but that night the cats had found her and had instinctively killed. Poor Sally! She may even have been on her way back to the box to see if there was a gecko inside it when she died. I looked at the kittens dozing innocently on the gauze, the carnage of Sally strewn about them, and could not be angry.

Sally was a nice snake; every other snake was not. We often saw them crossing the road—bright-green boomslangs, four feet long and with big, staring eyes, or small brown night adders, speedy and venomous. There was the green one that climbed up Manueri's leg and a large black cobra which we disturbed one day as it basked in a patch of sunlight deep in the forest. I myself shot three snakes with the .22. The smallest was a black-lipped cobra, sleek and black, a very slim five feet in length, with white bands under the head and neck. I came across it one evening while out looking for guinea-fowl. It lay like a stick in my path, then raised its head as I approached, giving itself away. I shot it in the neck and it died immediately, although it writhed involuntarily for some time. The second in size was a Gaboon viper, deadliest of Africa's snakes, which, while normally placid and therefore harmless, can, if it bites, kill a man in less than an hour. My shot did not kill it instantly, for it disappeared into tall grass and I had to leave searching for it until next morning. When we found it it was only two feet away, dead, but still writhing a little. The

snake was heavy and, even in death, still dangerous, for a
touch of its fangs could still kill. It was three feet six inches
in length and ten times as fat as the cobra. Its gape was wide
—to swallow the large forest rats on which it fed. The pattern
on its back was extraordinarily beautiful—blues, yellows, reds,
and blacks were balanced against each other in a symmetry
without parallel in the animal world or even perhaps in art;
the brightness of the colours meant that it had just changed
its skin. As we picked it out of the grass on that sunny African morning, the horror I felt at its fangs and gape, combined
with the ugliness of its arrow-shaped squashed-flat head with
little pig-eyes well concealed, together with the unquestion-
able extreme beauty of its skin along the length of the back,
inspired in me a sense of awe for the thing, which my African
helpers shared.

If I were to be asked why I killed these snakes, I would
have no trouble in answering and my answer would be completely truthful: I killed them because I did not want to run
the risk of meeting them again. It was as simple as that: dead
snakes do no harm. But in the case of my third snake, the
python, everything, from start to finish, was completely different. For a start, I did not bump into the snake, I was led
to it.

The story had started the night before. We were at home
having supper when a labourer from the Forest Department
came to the house. "Nyoka kubwa sana" he said it was, "a
very big snake," and I guessed it was a python. Would I come
next day to kill it? They would be grateful to me if I would
kill it, for they were working in the area and were scared of it.
I said I would come and look at it, but how could they be
sure to find it again? They said it would stay put.

That night I thought about the python, down in the forest, not knowing how dangerous his position was. In a way,
although I wanted to see him, I hoped he would move off so
that we would not find him. I had no desire to shoot a python,

for they are inoffensive towards man. I awoke determined that, if we found him, I would film him and leave him alone. Two men arrived and, accompanied by Manueri, we set off. The snake was deep in a part of the forest I did not know. It took an hour to reach the spot; ahead I heard the tracker cry "Iko!"—"It is here!" Coming to the spot I saw my python, his head raised angrily at the intruders, his sharply pointed, big tongue flicking in and out, tasting the smell of us, his terrible foe, perhaps the only animal he was afraid of. He was totally immobilised by a huge animal he had swallowed, and which now lay in his stomach distending him beyond belief. His head and a couple of feet of neck were free to move, the rest of his body behind the stomach lay coiled underneath him. He stared at us unceasingly. We stared back. I spoke to Manueri and the African trackers. "Hi nyoka muzuri, hapana kali. Hi hapana weza kukamata mutu"—"This is a good snake, not dangerous. It cannot kill man." They shook their heads. "Hi kali sana," they said—"It is very dangerous." "Mimi nataka piksha tu," I said—"I only want to take a photograph of it."

It was early yet. There was time to wait. The two men would get fed up with waiting and go off, then Manueri and I could go home. I told them I should be waiting there until the sun was high in the sky, then I could take a better photograph. They settled down to wait with us. It was a strange situation, us four men, me with a gun, they with knives, and this immense snake, more powerful muscle for muscle than any of us, but paralysed by its huge digestive capacity. We leaned against tree-trunks or on our elbows, waiting. The men puffed at cigarettes, and talked in Lunyoro. I watched the snake, which did nothing. Inside it was some sort of antelope. I could see the shape of the animal's head, which had gone down first, and the twin points of its horns, which were almost breaking through the python's skin. Then came the bulk of its body: swallowing that huge mass must have been as painful as having a baby.

I watched the forest coming to life, as it does every morning, its tempo and the hum of its insects increasing imperceptibly as the temperature rises. As always in the forest, the odd leaf fell, birds sang near and far away, giant motionless tree-trunks stood all around. Only this time there was the snake. And (I should have realised) patience is the African's virtue, it is the one thing he has in abundance, and it is a quality all white men lack, to greater or lesser extent. I set myself a deadline for departure at noon, and in its own good time noon arrived and the snake was still there digesting and the Africans were still there sitting and talking and I was still there. So I got up, took my photographs, called to Manueri and announced our departure. At this they were indignant and shocked. It would surely kill somebody; they wanted it dead. If necessary, one of them said, he would kill it with his panga. I looked to Manueri for support; he averted his eyes. That told me I was defeated. They would do it. I imagined the scene: it would be too terrible for words. I considered taking it alive, but we had nothing to put it in and it would be a colossal burden with that beast inside it. Added to which I had no experience in handling live pythons. Regretfully, after a lot of talk, I decided the most humane thing would be to kill it.

If I left it I would have its death on my mind anyway: better to do the job properly. I moved towards it with the gun raised. Alarmed, it suddenly struck out with its mouth open, displaying rows of white teeth, all its free neck lunging forward. Again and again it struck, so I had to aim from a distance, and even that was not easy, for I wanted a side shot and the snake kept its beady eyes on me. I felt it was imploring for mercy, pleading me to go away. Finally it looked away. I squeezed the trigger, despatching with that tiny bullet one of the most splendid creatures I have ever seen.

We carried it home strapped to a pole. It was eleven feet six inches long, eleven inches around the neck, thirty-three around the stomach. Then we skinned it; it had a pair of sharp claws, one on each side of the anus or genital opening, which, according to Manueri, were used not only in mating but also to grasp hold of the victim's nose, whereupon the snake would fill its nostrils with excrement and suffocate it. As we slit open the stomach there was revealed a fully grown female red duiker, almost undigested. The smell was awful. We left quickly; a few days later I returned to collect the teeth of the python, which had by then been picked clean by insects. I also took the duiker's skull; I am looking at that skull now as I write; its bone is blackened all over by the acid juices of the snake.

Few people know what mammals to expect when they walk into the forest. We ourselves had very little idea what we might see. For the forest fauna is very different from that of the surrounding plains: zebras and hartebeests and gazelles and sables and giraffes and rhinos and many of the other animals one thinks of as typically African, are absent. Lions and, oddly enough, hippopotami do occasionally occur in Budongo, but this is exceptional. The reason is not hard to find: Budongo lies at the top of an escarpment below which are Lake Albert and the three-mile-wide flatlands around the edge of the lake. These flatlands are typical open bush-country containing herds of antelopes and lions; hippos live in the lake itself. The odd lion or hippo which finds its way up to the forest has, for some reason, abandoned its home ground and headed eastwards. Elephants abound down on the flats and, being expert climbers, often come up the escarpment and into Budongo; in 1924 it was estimated that the forest supported a herd five thousand strong. But they do not stay in the forest all the time—there is a continual coming and going of elephants northwards of Budongo, probably as far as

Murchison Park, where they are fully protected and hence extremely numerous.

Most of the forest species of mammals, however, live in the forest and do not leave it. This is almost certainly true of the forest buffalo, which come out of the forest to rest in the tall elephant grass at its edges but browse inside the forest, where they make trails in the same way as elephants do. There are two kinds of buffalo in Africa, the red Congo buffalo of the forest and the large black buffalo of the plains. In Budongo the latter kind is found, showing that it is able to adapt to forest conditions. Buffalo did, however, seem to be most common in the Siba, where the forest is largely riverine and allows them easy access to the surrounding grassland. As elephants do with their tusks, buffalo damage trees by debarking them with their horns, and eat the tender rind of saplings, for I have found such trees stripped bare minutes after buffalo had left them.

Fortunately, we only once had a close brush with one of these great beasts. We had been making our way in silence towards some chimpanzees in particularly dense woodland forest when suddenly there was a thudding of feet and something rushed past us rather too close for comfort. We saw nothing.

"Hi nini?" I asked Manueri—"What is it?"

"Sijui, labda nyati"—"I don't know, perhaps buffalo."

All seemed quiet again so we went on; in due course we came up to the chimps and I remember we had just settled down to watch a mother and her youngster when the crashing started up again, and, again completely invisible, something big tore past us not more than ten yards away.

"Hi nyati moja, hi kali"—"That is one buffalo, it is dangerous," said Manueri. Without more ado he chipped a series of steps in a low tree by making one neat vertical and another horizontal cut, hauled himself up, and invited us to follow, which we did. All this was just too much for our mother chimp, who rapidly built a nest for herself and her baby and clambered into it. And for fifteen minutes or so there we all stayed, three scared humans in a small tree and one scared chimp up above. If the buffalo was watching from a nearby bush he might have been pardoned for a bovine expression of smug self-satisfaction. At all events, we heard no more of him.

Another animal which finds its whole living inside the forest is "chui," the leopard. Little is known about the habits of this secretive cat, and although I believe leopards are probably fairly common in Budongo, we were rarely favoured by a glimpse of one. Once we had been watching a group of chimpanzees for some minutes, high in the top of a tree nearby, when suddenly a loud rustling of leaves came from behind us; we looked round and saw first a duiker in headlong flight and then a leopard, some ten yards behind, chasing it in great bounds through the undergrowth. Neither of them saw us, and they were gone in a flash, yet this brief scene imprinted itself on our minds.

Manueri, returning one day on his own along Track A, came face to face with a big leopard in the act of eating a blue duiker. I wish I could describe the scene as he did: "The leopard looked at me, I looked at him. He growled. I had no panga, not even a small knife with me. But he wasn't hungry, he just wanted peace. I turned and walked away a few steps, I waited. The leopard got up, the duiker in its mouth, and walked off the track into the forest. Inside he growled. I heard him eating. I edged past the spot 'poli-poli' [very slowly], and then I ran!" He enacted every stage in the drama with gestures and expressions: we could imagine the scene very well. At the end came a moral: It is not good to walk in the forest with no knife, and he admonished himself for his stupidity. Armed with his panga, however, Manueri was unafraid of leopards, as we discovered on two separate occasions. The first time he came home one day with *half* a red duiker, the front half to be exact. I asked where the rest of it was and he said he had come upon a leopard having his dinner, shooed the leopard off, and grabbed the dinner. The second time we were deep in the forest, all three of us, when suddenly there was a dreadful scream quite close by. Without any hesitation, Manueri started off at high speed towards the scream, leaving us to follow. When he reached the spot where he thought it had come from, he stopped and looked all around and up in the trees, but he found no sign of anything, no blood, no signs of a scuffle anywhere. Manueri was certain we had heard a leopard making its kill and he wanted the meat. Perhaps we had. What we had definitely discovered was that Manueri was quite prepared to walk up to a leopard and dispute matters with it; whether this was bravado, folly, or an intimate understanding of jungle lore we were less sure.

Three species of antelope occur in Budongo, all fairly common. These are the bush-buck, the red duiker, and the blue duiker. Bush-buck spread beyond the forest into the surrounding savannah, but the duikers do not. All three are hunted with snares on a very large scale, although this is illegal and the game guards do their best to prevent it, by dismantling any snares they find. The ram bush-buck is, when fully adult, an extremely beautiful creature, standing some thirty-three inches high at the shoulders and with fine, gently curving horns rising upwards and outwards in the shape of a lyre. Known as the "swara," it provides a man with two months' food and is thus highly prized. We saw bush-buck quite often, sometimes very close to. Once, out looking for guinea-fowl, I turned a corner on a forest track and suddenly came face to face with a bush-buck, a fine adult male, not ten yards away. For a second or two we surveyed each other, and then he sprang into the trees, barking loudly in a deep, harsh, penetrating voice as he crashed through the shrubs. As he leaped I saw the fine white stripes along his sandy-coloured flanks, stripes which have the unusual feature that they do not occur in a fixed pattern, for some animals have few while others have many, and some have horizontal stripes as well as vertical ones, or even spots instead of stripes, breaking up the coat and thus providing camouflage.

The red forest duiker or "churo" is especially common in Budongo. Its coat colour is a deep rich russet all over; the male has straight, ringed horns about six inches in length, reaching fine points, and stands about eighteen inches high at the shoulder. Like all the duikers, the churo walks with its back curiously arched, giving it a hunched-up appearance. The alarm bark, which is all one normally knows of this elusive creature's presence, is a single repeated harsh note, higher pitched than that of the bush-buck. It is an ugly sound, strange, coming as it does from one of the forest's loveliest creatures, perhaps *the* loveliest. We rarely saw one for long, just fleeting glimpses as it crossed the track ahead of us or scampered through the trees. Once, however, as we were sitting silently waiting for chimpanzees to call, a pair came picking their way daintily along, stopping to snuffle in the leaves; they did not sniff us and went quietly on their way. Tragic that this lovely thing should be the tenderest, sweetest meat the forest has to offer: it was a sad tale which taught us this.

We were returning home from a day in the forest. I was out with a strange tracker that day, Manueri being ill with blisters on his feet. Suddenly we saw a red duiker by the side of the track, and as we looked we saw him trying to free his head with a hind leg. He was snared. As we approached he struggled violently, his eyes showing white, with a piteous fear of the men who were now closing in to murder him. I looked at him, and decided not to release him as his neck was sore from the rubbing wire and would fester, and he was bleeding around the face from trying to free himself. The tracker got a forked pole and pinned him down, then throwing him on his back I cut his throat with the panga, the only weapon we had. It was a horrible business and confirmed my belief that snaring is cruel; I was glad of the dozens of snares I had dismantled, some of them rusty with lack of visiting.

Having done the deed we handed the duiker over to the men, who were delighted. We kept a leg for ourselves, and discovered it was like veal, light in colour and fine-textured. I regret to say the horror of its end was quickly forgotten; nevertheless, I never hunted the red duiker despite its table qualities, for I had no desire to kill one as it picked its harmless way through the trees.

Equally fascinating was the blue forest duiker, one of the smallest of the ungulates. Thirteen inches high at the shoulder in the adult, with a pair of horns an inch long in the fullgrown male, this little blue-grey-coated creature wanders about the forest flicking its tail wherever it goes. There are thousands of them in the Budongo Forest, and they move around singly or in pairs, although on one occasion we saw four together and on another, six. The blue duiker, or "nende" as it is called, is a charming toy antelope, specially adapted to browsing on the very lowest level of vegetation, the delicate young leaves near the ground, leaving the higher ones to the red duiker and those higher still to the bush-buck. Once, in a rainstorm, a blue duiker sought shelter under the very tree where I was standing, and for a moment I felt that thrill of purity which St. Francis must have known, and which is shared to greater or lesser extent by everyone who has contact with wild animals. It was as if the duiker had no fear of me. Of course, the instant it sniffed me and caught my eye it was gone, flashing into the rain like an arrow. My illusion was shattered, and I was sad. Manueri in particular used to enjoy staying perfectly still as a nende came by. He would whistle softly to attract our attention and we would see his lips pointing. We would spot the animal walking along a few steps and then taking a bite, as all browsers and grazers do, a few more steps and another. Inevitably, at close range the duiker would smell us and, with hooves clattering over the sticks and leaves like the noise of a toy train, squeaking in a high-pitched, shocked voice, it would dash off into the trees.

As with the red duiker, it is a cruel paradox that such a lovely thing should be the chief target of humans with their snares, of leopards, and of the python. Between them, the duikers keep the forest's predators supplied with food—they are little more than walking dinners for the carnivores. Other species benefit from this: the monkeys and chimpanzees, the rats and shrews, and all the other forest creatures which might fall prey to the carnivores if it were not for the duikers. So their place in the jig-saw of forest life is very clear-cut—they are born to be crushed, bitten to death, and snared. Fortunately, they do not know this. Fortunately, perhaps, we none of us know the fate which awaits us. Yet it seems an irony of nature that she created them so beautiful. But beauty is in the eye of the beholder, and the irony is in the mind of the person who sees the beauty. To the local African, as to the leopard and python, a duiker is meat, the meat he craves, and he will go to great lengths to secure it.

One day a tall man was on our steps when we came home. In his arms he held a young churo. The sun was beating out of the sky and sweat was pouring off him. He said it would be tender and tasty; we were angry with him and thought of the mother. The baby duiker struggled feebly in his arms. We bought it and for the next week fought a losing battle to keep it alive. It was still on milk but we had no teat and no way of getting one. Our imitations with the use of gloves and other things did not work, but worse still, it clearly did not like the milk we were giving it, which was, on the advice of a local European who had successfully reared a duiker, half milk, made in our usual way with powder and water, and half water, with a dash of salt. The poor little thing hated this, much preferring my armpits, which must have smelled right but were, alas, utterly unable to provide him with milk. We knew we needed real milk. Nearby were some villagers who kept a herd of goats; they said that one of their goats had kids and that next day they would sell us a bottle of milk. But next day they said that it was impossible, the kids needed the milk and had taken it all. Our baby was weakening. The nearest herd of cows was fifteen miles away. We raced to the farm and waited until milking time at five o'clock. Arriving home we force-fed the duiker but we had little hope for its recovery. Later in the evening it had convulsive spasms and I could see it was suffering badly so I shot it. If we had taken it back to the forest when we first bought it, a mother might have heard its bleating and adopted it, but it might have fallen victim to a leopard or starved to death. Our mistake had been to feed it on dried full-cream milk which was not suitable for it; we had lined its stomach with fat, preventing further digestive processes. Naturally we had tried feeding it with solids but it never ate a thing, not even the tenderest young shoots we hopefully collected from the forest for it every day. It was just too young, and we told the man angrily he must not do it again—we did not want another baby, of any species. He must have been sorry, for next day he presented us with a tin-bowl of flowers.

A creature which died rather more suddenly was the edible rat which Manueri trapped on his own doorstep. I think he was trying to catch a bush-pig that used to come in the night and snuffle around on our refuse pile. He never succeeded. We did, however, get a wart-hog. A neighbour and I had been out looking for buffalo in the Siba—he was a big-game hunter and had a heavy rifle. On our way home we spotted two wart-hogs in the tall grass just outside the forest. He fired and got one. We heaved it into the Land Rover and, back at home, Manueri displayed his skill at butchery: the panga was all he needed. As with the duiker, we ordered a leg, and roasted it; the texture was like pork but the taste was a little strong, and reminded me of the smell of the animal when it was in the Land Rover, freshly killed. We did not finish the joint.

But to return to the bush-pig, or, to give it its more attractive name, the red river-hog. Quite unlike the wart-hog, this is a beautiful animal. We only once got a good view of one. It was a full-grown specimen, two and a half feet high, and it suddenly, without a sound, stepped out onto a forest track just ahead of us. It didn't see us as we stood, not twenty yards away in broad daylight, but came out confidently, showing off its bright orange-brown coat, and walked into the forest on the other side. In those few seconds my whole attitude to pigs was changed. I had now seen the stately majesty of a fine boar: our domestic pigs with their rolls of fat are hideously degenerate. The natural beauty of this hog, the ease and directness of his silent walk, was a far remove from the slobbering grunting swine of English sties. Once again, Manueri had no such fanciful ideas. He threw up his arms in despair as it calmly disappeared. "Wapi bunduki? Wapi bunduki?" he cried—"Where is the gun?" He had seen, in that pig, dried meat for himself and his friends for weeks. There was the difference. I was living off meat which I could afford to buy, although, of course, he could have afforded it too if he did less drinking. Manueri was in favour of my carrying a gun at all times and he frequently told me so. I told him it was an encumbrance, and this was perfectly true. But my real reason was that I did not want to let fly at every thing that moved; I was a conservationist and my stomach was well lined. Manueri's attitude was much less complicated.

Then there are the monkeys—four species in Budongo, and all of them common, so that you are almost certain to see them on any day spent in the forest. The little redtail monkey ("kunga") is the most charming, with its snow-white nose in the middle of a black face, trim moustache, white cheeks, and long rusty-coloured tail. Always affronted by your presence, they sit chirping like birds and making rapid movements of the head, running a little way, intensely curious and not a little scared. If you pass on they do not scamper away, but they dislike being looked at and quickly head off into the trees if you stop. We only once clearly saw one of these on the ground; it walked with its long tail held vertically and curled over forwards at the tip. Much is known about the redtail monkey, thanks largely to the efforts of Alec Haddow, who made a special study of its behaviour, during which he discovered that it played a part in the transmission of yellow fever by mosquitoes to man.

A close relative of the redtail is the larger blue monkey, locally known as "kima." A shy creature, its coat colour is grey-blue all over, with a black crown, and just below this, in front, a very distinctive white stripe above the eyes. Very little is known about this species. A fruit-eater, like the redtail, here in Budongo it spends much of its life in the trees. Once again, there was only one occasion when we saw a blue monkey on the ground: it was deep in the forest, and as he fled up into a tree just ahead of us we mistook him for a black leopard! But Manueri found his footprint and no scratch marks on the tree, and there he was, just above us, an ordinary kima. He was one of the big males which grow to a very great size and are often found away from others of their kind. I believe that we were among the first people to observe sexual behaviour in this species, for there are no reports in the literature. One morning in bright sunlight at 8:45 A.M., high up in a tree-top, a female presented to a male which came up; he mounted her briefly, and then followed her closely and finally groomed her. On two occasions we saw groups of blue monkeys all of which were youngsters, so it looks as if there may be "age-grades" in this species. Besides a chirping note similar to the redtail's there is an alarm call, a distinctive, loud "kyoh!" and another call "ko . . . ko . . . ko . . . ko . . . ," a sort of animated croaking, the function or meaning of which is completely unknown.

The black-and-white colobus monkey ("engeye") is our Budongo showpiece—the film star of the forest, beautifully clad in a robe of black with a fleecy white mantle around the shoulders and along the back, and a long black tail with a white tassel at the end. The colobus is a very distant relative of the redtails and blues, being in fact closer to the langur monkeys of India than to these African species. It eats leaves and not fruit, moves about the tree-tops by leaping and not by running as the others do, has no thumbs, and possesses the oddest-looking face—like a dark monk peering out of a white cowl with a black skull-cap on his head. Shyer even than the blue monkey, the colobus crashes off through the canopy with an agility which must be seen to be believed. It readily leaps anything up to thirty feet from tree to tree, can run down a tree-trunk *head first*, and members of a group always follow each other along exactly the same route, hiding among the shadowy leaves until it is their turn, and then moving so fast it is hard to see them. When at rest, however, this is a charming animal, which, if not busily feeding on the tender leaftips of vines and creepers, sits in pairs or threes just dozing side by side, or, if a youngster is present, putting up with its onslaughts as it plays. Once we noticed an adult colobus, which was being pestered in this way, switch its tail to and fro just like a cat. But the most staggering thing about this animal is its call—a long, deep, vibrating gargle, repeated anything up to fifty times. It is much more like a frog's croaking and when we first searched for the source of the noise I remember we had our eyes to the ground looking for some giant bull-frog. According to Manueri, the colobus gargles at six in the morning and six in the evening, and quite often this was the case. But it also gargles at other times, and I can make it do so. There, deep in the forest, I found a use for a habit I had secretly developed in London, despite all the strictures of society to the contrary: the habit (approved, I may say, by the Emperor Claudius) of belching loudly after a meal. One day, as we sat among the leaves having lunch, swallowing the last doughy remnants of our squashed bread and chew-

ing out the last bit of goodness from some very gristly beef,
I let rip and was immediately answered by a colobus several
hundred yards away. It worked again on other occasions, and
I think the explanation may be that the colobus is a terri-
tory-minded monkey, and is quick to outdo any gargling in
his area with gargling of his own.

Our last monkey is the olive baboon. Dog-faced, noisy,
cheeky, curious: we all know baboons. Here in Budongo they
are often seen in troops of enormous size, too big to count,
for one never sees all the animals. At night they sleep in trees,
but by day they wander along the forest floor eating the
pithy stems of shrubs, digging up roots, and quarrelling occasionally. They sometimes clamber up into trees to eat the
fruits, tumbling out of them with neither poise nor grace as
we come along. On the ground they are more confident, peeping through the leaves at us, tossing their heads and stamping
their feet as if incensed, while a big male barks ceaselessly at
us in a dog-like voice. It is hard to love a baboon unless, I
suppose, you are a baboon; but it is easy to laugh at them,
especially when Manueri starts talking to them. Putting his
hand to his lips, he imitates superbly the noise of a frightened baby—a high-pitched, whining, squealing sound—and the
response is immediate. The baboons get agitated, they look
and look, taking up new vantage points, crowding closer all
the time, anxious to see if we have caught a youngster and
are holding it by the tail.

Unlike their cousins in La Fontaine's fables and so many
delightful children's stories, the various species of animals in
the Budongo Forest kept rather aloof from one another, coming together, as in the case of the monkeys and birds and butterflies, to feed on a common food, but otherwise moving
around alone or with others of their own kind. Perhaps some
species could recognise the alarm calls of other species. For
example, on one occasion we were quietly watching a big

mother chimpanzee and her "toto" (baby) when from close by there came three loud coughs of a bush-buck which had probably caught our scent. The mother looked attentively towards the sound, then took her baby below her belly and descended. She had been alone, and anyway mothers are more than usually careful.

But it was food which acted as the magnet bringing different kinds of animals together. Blue monkeys and redtail monkeys, both fruit-eaters, were often together or with chimpanzees in the same tree, while the colobus monkeys, with their diet of leaves, were usually out of the party. But the baboons, although they eat fruit, were never seen with groups of these smaller monkeys, because they are a dominant species, so that, when they arrived with their noisy screeching and bullying manner, the other monkeys scampered away. And here it was interesting for us to note that the chimpanzees, while so much stronger than the baboons, would mix and feed with the smaller monkeys but would move a short way off, in a dignified manner, when the baboons arrived, as if they found their company distasteful. Thus, our chimpanzees left a tolerance-radius of one tree-span between themselves and baboons, but they allowed individual redtails to come as close as five yards and blue monkeys as close as three yards. Then, however, their patience was exhausted and with a little threatening jerk they chased the cheeky monkey away. And some of the monkeys, especially the redtails, were cheeky. They would run along a branch where an unsuspecting chimpanzee sat feeding and jump right over him, or zip under his nose as fast as they could, but we never saw a chimpanzee get angry to the point of chasing a monkey— it was beneath his dignity, one felt, not worth the effort, and anyway it would be doomed to failure in the end as the featherweight monkey leapt along little branches which would send a chimpanzee crashing to the ground. With blue monkeys we saw something which had been reported in the past: a single large apparently male monkey moving around with a group of chimpanzees. We saw this on several occasions, always in the trees, and could never establish for sure whether, when the chimps moved off along the ground on one of their tracks, the kima moved along with them or kept up above them in the trees. Perhaps he didn't travel with them at all. For lone males are known in many species of monkeys, and it is quite possible that, attracted by the calls of the chimpanzees (which he knows from experience mean that food is abundant), and knowing that the big black apes will tolerate him in the tree with them, he turns up and starts feeding with them, and that is where we find him. More evidence is needed before we can say that he moves with them from place to place.

Apart from these monkeys, the chimpanzees have little contact with other species except that they are continually bumping into them as they move about the forest. With their silent tread they must often come up against duikers; they must see snakes from time to time; birds are never far away in the tree-tops; ants they eat occasionally; leopards, we think, do not bother them, preferring tastier morsels; and their response to elephants and buffaloes we never could determine.

Sometimes they run into an unfortunate animal caught in a snare, and Manueri had a fascinating story to tell of this. I had been discussing with him the question of whether the Budongo chimpanzees ever ate meat. He denied this emphatically and related as follows. One day four years ago he had set a snare to catch a duiker. On returning to it he saw that it had been interfered with—by men, he thought. As he was leaving in disappointment, he heard a noise in the trees and, looking up, saw a chimpanzee holding a dead duiker in its arms and tossing it up and down. Manueri went away and returned the following day; the duiker had fallen to the bottom of the tree, it had not been bitten into; he himself ate it that evening. Coming from a stranger I would have passed this off as a bit of fanciful story-telling, but from Manueri I believed it. We had often watched duikers picking their dainty way beneath a group of feeding chimpanzees, which never took any interest in them. But a struggling, snared duiker might well be expected to arouse their curiosity. Perhaps a whole band, running into the victim, had gathered excitedly around, hooting and thumping, maybe even pulling at the duiker and finally breaking its neck. One of the more curious of them, not wanting to part with such a prize, could have pulled it out of the snare and dragged it up the tree, given it a thorough examination, and then dropped it.

Who knows? The forest is full of surprises.

CHAPTER FIVE

Days and Nights

Just as the equatorial sun starts and ends his day with a grand regularity, so on our own smaller scale we imposed a pattern on our days to fit in with the sun. Our morning routine was especially impressive. It went like this: at six o'clock Semei's alarm clock (which we had loaned him) rang (if it was wound up). He then (if he heard it) went down to the outside kitchen and loaded the Dover stove with "kuni"—bits of fire-wood—which, when dashed, soused, or flooded with paraffin (depending on how damp the wood was) usually caught fire. By six-thirty Frankie and I were up. It was now beginning to grow light enough to see. Dressing quickly, and fixing her make-up by candlelight with a tiny piece of shattered mirror, Frankie went backstage to supervise the breakfast while I cleaned my teeth thoroughly, a thing I enjoy doing very much and which does not suffer from using boiled water. I then made my way to the verandah, which was the one and only place to be at dawn. There I pottered about, cleaning binoculars and checking films, taking temperature readings with a whirling cyclometer (before I broke it), and listening all the while for early chimpanzee calls from the forest.

By a quarter to seven, all being well, huge mugs full of friendly steaming tea appeared. We swallowed down our anti-

malarial Paludrine pills and started on the bacon, which, however charred, had that special flavour without which no Eng-
lishman can honestly face the day. On top of this we had
toast—Frankie made the bread, and we had brought with us
a little square grid, bought in Woolworths, which made excellent toast—and marmalade. These dawn breakfasts on the
verandah were our greatest luxury. The cool morning air gave
us hunger, and as it grew light and the mist-furrowed forest
could be seen below, we wondered idly what the day would
bring. At seven the sun appeared redly just opposite us over
the forest. It was the moment to leave. I called "Manueri!"
and heard the muffled answer from his hut, "Bwana!" In an
instant he was with us, panga in hand, and after saying
"Jambo" and sharing out the load, we headed down the steps
to start the day.

The load varied from day to day. Our basic necessities
were compasses, binoculars, and the lunch bag, which also
contained our plastic macs, Caladryl (anti-itch) cream, maps,
knife, notebook, pencil, and the Fitzsimons Anti-Snake Bite
Kit. Lunch consisted of a beef sandwich each and a small bottle of boiled water. It was no use taking more: bulk and weight
were our enemies, on top of which the meat was tough and
tasteless and the bread doughy. Apart from these basics, I
sometimes took either the still camera or the movie camera
or the tape recorder (until it went wrong). These latter two
were heavy items and when I did take them Manueri and I
took turns at carrying them. The biggest nuisance of all was
the heavy tripod I required with the movie camera, which,
however it was carried, managed to get itself tangled with
every hanging liana and vine we passed. Thus, most of the
time these heavy items stayed at home.

Depending on how far we were going along the road, we
either took the Land Rover or set off on foot, but most days
the chimpanzees were not close by. If we knew where to find
them from the previous evening, well and good; otherwise we

had to start by visiting "listening points" along the edge of the forest and inside it along the tracks. We drove a half mile, then stopped, got out, and sat down to listen, for ten or fifteen minutes at each point. There was nothing we could do about this waste of time; if we had no idea where the chimpanzees were, we just had to wait for them to announce themselves. We had some very frustrating days, quite a number of them, when we sat about all morning looking glum, as the forest warmed up around us and our chances of hearing anything grew slimmer and slimmer, for chimpanzees are noisier and their calls carry further in the early morning than later on. But most days our perseverance was rewarded, and we would hear the faint familiar sound through the trees and I would check with Manueri—"Soko-mutu?"—and he would say "Iko"—"Here," pointing with finger or lips, and we would decide whether they were "karibu, karibu kidogo, mbale kidogo, mbale, or mbale sana"—"near, a little near, a little far, far, or very far"—while I took a compass bearing. Then, with an inevitability which had a strange pleasure for us, we began the long trek that might or might not lead us to the chimps.

Manueri went first, I second, and Frankie third; it was always the same. Once or twice when Manueri disagreed with the compass I took the lead. It happened like this. We might have been following a moving band of chimpanzees round in a circular path until we were in fact facing the opposite way from the way we had come in. Or we might have taken a zigzag path through the forest following first one band and then another and then a third. Sooner or later we would decide to abandon the chase and return home. During the day Frankie would keep track of every bearing we followed and the approximate distance we covered on that bearing. This she drew on a page in our notebook, and at the end of the day we had a fair idea which direction would take us back to our starting point. Manueri, on the other hand, had only his innate sense of direction to rely on, and, while it was better than ours, it was decidedly fallible. So when the moment of truth arrived, and with a confident gesture I held out my arm in the direction of home and said "Let's return," Manueri would head off in a different direction with equal confidence and expect us to follow him. On these occasions a maximum of tact was necessary, and I had also to bear in mind that we might, just conceivably, have used the compass wrongly. Manueri had spent fourteen years wandering in that forest, and although he could still get completely lost in it, he considered this impossible and an outrageous suggestion. So the conversation went something like this:

"Wait a little. We want to go there," I say, pointing.

"No," he replies, shaking his head vigorously. "That way will take us deep into the forest, we want to return to the Land Rover. The Land Rover is here," pointing to where he thinks it is.

"No, that way is the big forest. The road is here." I follow the line of the compass needle with my arm.

"No. You go that way. I'm going back to the Land Rover. I know the forest."

"Yes, I know you know the forest. However, it is not me who knows you are wrong, it is the compass. Compass says: this way." Shelving all responsibility onto the little black box in my hand. Very neat.

But the first few times it didn't work at all. "Compass rongo," he asserted, and it was absolutely impossible to shift him. So, the first few times, before I learnt better, we followed him on his chosen route, against all the dictates of compass and map, until, exhausted and his confidence weakened, he was beginning to doubt the wisdom of going on along a route which should have brought us to our track hours ago. Choosing my moment with some care I would say, "Manueri, you are taking us deep into the forest. Follow me." And turning about, Frankie following, without another look at him, we walked away. Argument was futile in these cases, for Manueri just lost dignity as he racked his brain for reasons to justify his direction, which even he himself no longer believed in. As time went on his respect for the compass grew and he thought carefully before arguing with it. "Compass knows, it knows very well," he said, and, entering into the spirit of this new navigational aid, he would even stop from time to time and ask, "Here, or here?" It was a great victory for modern science.

The fear which dominates all others in the forest is the fear of getting lost. Manueri told us the following story. It was in the days when he was working for the Forest Department, and he would go out every day with his fellow workmen, deep into the forest to tend the trees. I wish I could tell the story in his own words, with the expressions of his face and pauses for effect. The men were walking through the trees when suddenly they spotted a creature sitting at the foot of a big tree; it was like a man only deathly thin, crouched up, with the skin clinging to the bones, and big dark eyes which gazed steadily out at the approaching men. "Eeee! Ahh!" they exclaimed, pointing; and then they ran as hard as they could back to the work camp. It was "satani ya kibrani"—"the devil of the forest," a being which is terribly dangerous to meet. They told their story to the forest ranger, an educated man, who decided to investigate. Reaching the spot, the ranger announced to the cowering men: "This is no devil, this is so-and-so, the man who got lost three months ago." It was, indeed, one of an earlier working party who had got lost in the forest and had been given up for dead. They lifted him up. He was light as a feather, his legs and arms were stiff and would not move, and yet he was alive. They took him to the hospital and he recovered and is now working at the mill. It was a miracle he had not been eaten by a leopard or, worse, by ants.

I do not know how many victims the forest claims every year. Probably not many, for men go into the forest in pairs or groups and very rarely alone, and women go in very rarely indeed. People are said to get lost most frequently when going for elephant meat after a kill. They decide to take a short-cut and are not heard of again. But these local Africans, for the most part, leave the forest well alone and it is only the desire for meat which takes them into it.

Sometimes as we walked through the forest we used to imagine what it must be like to be lost, perhaps in order to prepare ourselves for that eventuality. I remember a conversation with Manueri on the subject.

"If we were lost, completely, what would we do?"

"We would go in a line, straight until we got out of the forest."

"And if that did not work?"

"We would look for tracks."

"And if there were no tracks?"

"We would listen for sounds from the road."

"And if there were no sounds?"

"Then we would be lost completely."

"And what would we eat?"

"Ah, man cannot eat the fruit of the chimpanzee. We would eat mushrooms, and I would snare duikers."

"And if you had no wire?"

"Then I would use a creeper."

"And if we could not get food?"

Manueri was not entirely pessimistic. It would be good, I felt, to have him around if we ever did get lost. Take those mushrooms he had mentioned, for instance. We had already found some once before; one day, walking through a glade we knew well, we had been surprised to see the whole of the forest floor covered with a white mantle, which, on examination, turned out to be made up of thousands of tiny white mushrooms, their little heads perched daintily on tall white succulent stems. "Oh, mahoga muzuri!"—"Good mushrooms!" said Manueri, and set to work collecting them by the

handful until our bag was crammed full. "Mimi tarudi ke-
sho," he said—"I shall return tomorrow," and then a thought
worried him: "Labda nyamangogoto takuja"—"Perhaps tor-
toises will come." According to Manueri, these mushrooms
were the favourite diet of the tortoise. Returning to our
theme, however, I doubt whether, without Manueri's assur-
ance that they were good, we should ever have picked any
of those little mushrooms at all, for fear of agonising death
by poison. As it was we all had a wonderful feast.

But, I am glad to say, we never got seriously lost. At times
the situation looked hopeless and we certainly knew the fear
that grips one when, hour after hour, the familiar, long-
awaited track one is heading for fails to show up. One problem
was that our rate of progress was so variable, depending on
how thick the forest was. So that, even though we knew the
various bearings we had followed, and the time spent following each, we never had any clear idea of how far we had gone
on each bearing; in short, we never knew exactly where we
were.

I remember one occasion when we were in the swamp-forest of the Siba, a part we had hitherto avoided, miserable
slushy forest with bilharzia-ridden streams and spiny rattans
everywhere and giant curtains of cobweb hanging like closely
woven muslin from the trees. In that gigantic swamp the
trees themselves were covered in great spikes, sticking out like
daggers all around the trunk. Why any tree should need such
massive armaments I could not imagine—was there a time
when giant beasts waded through these swamps, curling their
tongues around every sapling which did not resist? Or perhaps it was elephant protection. There certainly were elephants
in this part of the forest, for their heavy tracks were abundant.
Tree ants in millions lived in the swampy undergrowth, and
fell on us in black showers whenever we cut through a thick
patch of rattan and shook them off their arboreal highways.
They fell down our necks and got tangled in our hair, and

each little devil bit until it was killed. Their nests hung like big black soccer-balls in the bushes. We stopped in a glade to rest; the chimpanzees were on the move and leading us a merry dance through the swamps. They called ahead quite close and we moved on. The day was hot and the swamp less cool than true forest, as the canopy was thinner. We got close to the chimpanzees but they eluded us; we dodged this way and that, determined to close the gap between us.

The ants by now were driving us mad, and our legs were soaked in vile swamp-water which we knew would bring our skin up in blisters. Manueri was as tired as we were. We sat down to have lunch and rest. No sooner had we taken the first bite than there was a movement on the ground ahead of us and a knocking of branches. We listened carefully. We had never heard this noise before. Manueri whispered, "Hi tembo" —"That's elephant." We looked at him incredulously. If it was true it was bad, and we did not intend to establish whether it was true or not. Packing our half-eaten lunch, we silently melted away in the direction of home. Settling down again half a mile away, Manueri beat a tree with the side of the blade of his panga: the noise rang out like a rifle-shot, and in the distance we heard animals crashing through the trees. It was a trick he had learned for scaring them, but one that could only be used at a safe distance.

After lunch we went on, and it was only then that we re-alised the extent of our troubles. For walking along our home-ward bearing we suddenly came to the edge of the forest, an ocean of elephant grass where nothing but forest should have been. On the far side of the grass the forest began again. We had to decide whether to cross the grass or go around the edge in the swamp. The compass pointed resolutely across the grass. Manueri pointed another way which I felt sure was wrong. I hated that swamp, hated the gnawing feeling that I was being impregnated with worms at every sodden foot-fall even more than the rattan splinters and the ants.

"I know where the Land Rover is," I said, perhaps to convince myself. "It is over there. We shall cross the grass. Follow me." It was a decision born of ignorance, fear, and ill-temper. The sheer misery of crossing that field of grass was my reward. Every step had to be prepared, by pushing down the wall of grass which rose fifteen feet ahead of me. Cutting it with the panga was futile, there was simply too much. And pushing it down meant that with every push my fingers and knuckles were filled with fine prickles from the grass, which quickly became sores. And the heat outside the forest was so intense that after a hundred yards, with the distant trees not a whit nearer, the sweat was pouring off me and blinding my eyes. There were ants in the grass too. Suddenly I pushed down the wall and was surprised to find the way ahead for ten yards or so already prepared—it looked as if a steam-roller had been over the ground. "Nyati," said Manueri, in his blasé style for use on occasions of tension—"Buffalo." I shrugged and went on. Now every time I pressed at the wall I expected to hear a snort and see a great black sleeping form rise up and greet me with a toss of horns. Half way across the grass I almost fell over with exhaustion and fear.

Without a word, Manueri came forward and began to tackle the grass. As always, he had a better way of doing it—with his left arm he pulled the grass over sideways and with a cut from the panga made a thin channel for us to walk through. We finished the journey in due course, and sank back into the cool forest with relief. Now I no longer challenged Manueri's leadership—this had been his victory and he was in charge. We were completely lost, and our bearings too, and we were too weary to care. He led us along a river, for miles it seemed, and suddenly we came across a woman washing clothes, her naked children clinging to her dark-green dress in fear as they peeped at us, at our bedraggled hair and bleeding hands wrapped in handkerchiefs and backs wet with sweat. We sat down and Manueri talked to her. Above us redtail monkeys chirped and groomed each other, and from nearby we heard the sound of people. We had lost our way all right, but thank God we had run into a village. Manueri sat still, perfectly composed, talking as if he had just got up after a good afternoon's rest.

"Where are we?" I said. "Do you know this place?"

"I know it," he replied, "this is where I used to live."

At the end of the day's work in the forest a new routine comes into play. Dragging ourselves wearily up the forty-odd steps to our house, we drop onto chairs exhausted while Semei fixes us a well-earned mug of tea. After this, and revived by an all-over wash in cold water and a complete change of clothes, I settle down to copy our field notes from the pocket book into our big chimpanzee log, a job which often takes a couple of hours; also any leaf or fruit samples collected during the day have to be pressed or bottled. As dusk falls the Tilley is lit and I work on by its hot hissing radiance, among a bombardment of dudus from the forest night, while delicious smells of stew waft through from the kitchen and find me on the verandah. Generally we sup by candlelight as it is less hot than the Tilley, and fewer insects get into the food. Meanwhile hyraxes call from the trees below and a tropical moon, wisped over now and then by slow-moving clouds, gazes down at our humble spread. We open a bottle of beer and sip it lovingly, revelling in the soft cool of the night wind as it brushes our bare arms and necks. Most evenings, some late calls of chimps come to our ears.

We talk of anything, but often we try to compare this strange life of ours with that dimly-remembered one we led in London, to which we know with certainty we are fated to return. We ask ourselves: what is it that makes the contentment we feel, living out here in the African bush? The climate is harder to bear than it was at home, with its continuous succession of humid hot days that sap your strength. We work longer hours here, from dawn to dusk most days. Despite the fact that we eat enough, we are both steadily losing weight and our clothes hang about us. We aren't masochists though, or never used to be—so why do we like this life?

Perhaps it is because we are not hemmed about by doubts and guilts. If you get up at dawn, there is no self-recrimination about starting the day late, wasting valuable time. In London, every day for years, we started almost each day with the feeling we were in a hurry, late. This is not to advocate that everyone in London should get up at dawn, but simply to state that getting up at dawn is more satisfying than getting up at any other time. For there was definitely a time in our ancestry when our forefathers lived the same daily cycle as the monkeys and chimpanzees do now, waking at dawn and going to sleep at dusk, and this rhythm is inherent in us and satisfying to perform. Man seems, however, to have reached a stage where eight hours of sleep are sufficient, while the monkeys and chimpanzees in our forest sleep for twelve. Thus man can and does stay awake and active for four hours after dusk here on the equator. How he has achieved this is unknown—perhaps he finds and grows foods of greater nutritive value during the daylight hours than the vegetable diet of the gathering monkeys, thus enabling him to remain active longer and reduce the period of energy-conserving sleep. At all events the guilt-feelings resulting from getting up late are not paralleled at the end of the day—going to bed at dusk after twelve waking hours leads to no satisfaction, while staying awake, sitting around the fire or Tilley lamp, drinking and talking in the warm black night air, is one of the pleasantest experiences we know.

Doubt, too, is lacking from our life out here. Not just petty doubts, about whether to take the bus or the tube for example, but doubts about the meaning of life, the wisdom of staying in one's particular job. Here these problems do not exist: we are too involved in the work and the business of living to give the matter a thought. For there is no possibility of changing jobs—quite apart from our obligations to the university, there isn't another job in Uganda we would rather do. How different it is in London, where there are always other jobs which seem to offer just that little more sparkle and remuneration than one's own. As to the meaning of life, we have not solved that one, but we are holding it at bay, too engrossed in living to think about it. At home life did not hold us so firmly in its grip and so our minds were more detached and philosophical; here we do not ponder deep matters. We ponder the social life of chimpanzees, the toughness of the meat, the tick which has buried itself in our groin.

It is a fact that our life in Africa is a good deal more real and purer than life in the big city. That world, at home, was composed totally of make-believe: we talked about television, plays, films, books, "famous" people, and so on. So insulated were we from dangers that, like the captive raccoon which "washes" his food in his water-bowl because in the wild he would catch it in a stream, we sought them out on the television screen or in the mad speed of the big dipper. And when reality struck: death to a near-one, an accident or illness to ourselves, we were bowled over, it was hard or impossible to comprehend. In Africa death and disease and accident are never far away. We take our anti-malarial pills each morning, but against such diseases as bilharzia we have no protection except a little knowledge. One day or another, each of us meets his snake, or an elephant on the road; we hear the leopard's coughing grunt in the forest; we feel the pinch when food stocks fail to arrive; we fall ill. Our lives, like those of all other animal species, lack guilts and doubts but are closely circumscribed by fear.

But we are tired and the heavy scents of the flower trees in the garden make us drowsy. Shutting the door behind us, we grope our way through to our stone bedroom and within minutes are in our sleeping bags on deliciously comfy safari camp-beds, fast asleep.

For some time we had had the idea of spending a week or so inside the forest by night instead of by day. The advantage of this was that we would be able to watch the chimpanzees making their nests, and be in position again next morning to watch them getting up. We had found this difficult up to now as we generally had to leave the chimps before they made their nests in order to be out of the forest by dusk, and the difficulties of getting into the forest before dawn without making any noise had defeated us. The game warden at Masindi, John Heppes, had authorised us to take along the two local game guards, Okenyi and Okello; it was simply a matter of giving them the word.

One day we felt in need of a change from our routine, and so I went down the road that evening to Okenyi's home and discussed the matter with him. He agreed to start next day; I told him we should leave at 4 P.M. I would locate some chimpanzees during the early afternoon, and we would try to intercept them later and follow them to their sleeping place. Frankie set to work preparing the rucksacks.

When we set off there were seven of us: the game guards and their porters, us two, and Manueri; we looked like a guerrilla patrol, dressed in khaki, bristling with arms, walking in single file and without speech through the forest. I had found some chimpanzees which now called in the distance, and we made a bee-line for them. Manueri went first, followed by the guards, myself, and Frankie, with the porters bringing up the rear. We moved along as silently as seven people can, but still I felt we were making as much noise as a bull elephant. Our months of tracking had made us noise-conscious; we knew how to step over twigs that might snap and could tell when a twig was damp and would not crack but just disintegrate, and we knew also that every so often one accidentally makes a noise. Now our numbers were doubled and we each had a pack on our backs and the net result was a constant succession of nerve-racking snaps and crackles.

The afternoon was hot after the rain, streams flowed along the valleys we crossed, and as each man reached the water he bent down and scooped a handful to his mouth and drank it, then another, and wet his sweating face and neck with a third. We two did not touch the water if we could help it, for, rightly or wrongly, we did not trust it. We knew that our pampered civilised bodies reacted violently to things which the local Africans took in their stride, malaria for instance, or dysentery. Their systems had become tough and resistant through constant infection and re-infection; if they had not, these men would have sickened or even died as children, the natural fate of many of Africa's sons and daughters, which checks her population growth despite the high birth rate.

As we approached the chimpanzees, which seemed fortunately to be settled and not on the move, I looked around for somewhere to camp. It was essential that we should stop short of them and not disturb them; they would literally run a mile at the sight of this expeditionary force. Finally, in a natural glade with a troop of colobus monkeys gargling beside us, we came to a halt and put down our burdens. We lit cigarettes and chatted in low voices. The plan was to wait until about an hour before dusk and then, if the chimpanzees were still in position, to put up our tents and hammocks on the safe assumption that they would not move far before sleeping. So at five-thirty, when they could still be heard close ahead, we arranged our gear. The men quickly had their tents up, but we had a little trouble with our hammocks, which, owing to our lack of experience and the irregular spacing of the trees, never seemed to be quite right. Finally we got them lashed up side by side about three feet off the ground, and I demonstrated my faith in my carefully constructed non-give knots by climbing rather gingerly into each hammock in turn and bouncing up and down in it. Leaving Frankie to put the finishing touches to our arboreal beds, Manueri and I set off towards the chimps.

It was a painfully slow walk as we simply had to avoid any risk of disturbing them. Every tree was given a notch with the panga, and after every few steps we stopped and peered into the trees ahead. We soon found them, and took up positions behind large trees to watch them build their nests. This proved unexpectedly difficult. For a start, it was only possible to watch one chimpanzee, the nearest one, as we did not want to manoeuvre about in search of a good position from which we could see several chimps, but from which we might later not be able to find our way back in the dark to our track and to camp. However, we did get a good view of the nest-building process, and stayed watching until just the odd hand and arm could be seen over the rim of the nest making little adjustments, and the chimpanzees nearby were giving their final hoots and calls for the day. Perhaps they were locating each other, or simply responding to the pleasant bedtime feeling. There was nothing harsh or shrill about these late calls; they were most musical.

Suddenly Manueri and I realised it had grown very dark on the forest floor. Looking up towards the tree-tops had deceived us, down below all was inky black. We started the homeward trip and almost immediately got lost. Our little white marks on the trees would have had to be luminous to help us. We floundered about, as silently as we could, thinking silent curses as we tripped on lianas. At last we heard a cough from ahead, it sounded human, in fact it sounded rather like Okenyi. We crept forward towards the sound, feeling our way and bumping into each other. A little flicker of light reached us through the trees; in a moment we were sitting round the oil-lamp, relieved at not having got stupidly lost a hundred yards from camp. Vigorously we tucked into our sandwiches.

A final cigarette was smoked. Frankie informed me that the site I had selected for pitching camp was beside a huge dead tree. We inspected it and prayed for a calm night.

After that we all went to bed. The Africans went to sleep instantly. We were still shifting about in our hammocks, which insisted on hanging at an angle, ready to pitch us out to the right or the left the moment we stirred in our sleep. Perhaps it was the way we had hung them. Finally we decided to lump it. We lay back trustingly, keeping as still as we could. It was night, the pitch-black night of the forest. We did not know whether there was a moon in the sky, or whether the stars were twinkling brilliantly above. Everything was blotted out.

From the tent where our protectors lay came irregular snores. I think we had imagined that the guards would take it in turns to stay awake, rifle at the ready, poking a dying fire every now and then and making it flare up again. I think we had imagined a mutter of voices all night long, and the glimmer of dark bodies around the fireside. No such luck! The fire was out, the guards were safely tucked up inside their splendid Game Department tent, and Manueri was in his. We alone were exposed for any passing beast to take a sniff and a nibble at. Were we afraid?

Oddly enough, not at all. There were noises around us, of tree hyraxes and owls, and some strange ghostly sounds and some squeaking, but no terrifying roars or growls. We quickly went to sleep, comforted by the regular peaceful snores of the guards. Several times in the night the chimps called out loudly and woke us up. Once I awoke to find a creature snuffling about in our bags below the hammocks—it might have been a duiker or a pig, a civet or a porcupine, there was no way of knowing. But I felt no fear—rather I felt a certain intimacy with this creature just below me. I do not know why, but the thought that it might, just conceivably, be a leopard never entered my drowsy mind.

Towards dawn a wind got up, and we thought of the tall dead giant standing on the edge of our camp-site. Had destiny arranged a meeting between us? It would have been a complete disaster for us if that tree had fallen, and we almost deserved it for our stupidity. But though the wind blew hard and shrill in the tree-tops, nothing fell, not even a branch, and our fears were relieved. With the wind came a little rain and we pulled plastic macs over our bodies, leaving our faces to get wet. We had not needed our mosquito netting—not a dudu had bothered us all night. At six the alarm clock in my pocket went off; we staggered out of "bed" and roused our companions, who emerged sleepily and in a fairly good humour. Groping about for our immediate needs—binoculars and so on—in the exact places where they had been thoughtfully placed the night before but no longer were, we finally got ourselves ready to leave. We were glad to notice that sleeping in hammocks had left our bodies supple, in sharp contrast to the bruised, stiff feeling one has after sleeping on the ground. We looked at the sky, which was beginning to lighten through the tree-tops. No-one spoke. Okello wound the khaki puttees around his legs. He still had one leg to do but we could not wait—he could catch us up. Manueri announced that he could now see, and without more ado we set off towards our first white mark.

The new method brought its rewards. In position at last, we scrutinised the tops of the saplings where we knew a chimpanzee was sleeping. Each of us was well concealed behind a big tree. For minutes nothing happened and we thought the chimp might have heard us the night before and hurried off in a panic to nest elsewhere. Then, unexpectedly from one side, came a first hoot, a greeting to the day, followed by a tree-top cough, discreet, rather out of place at that time of day—more like the evening coughs which are heard between movements of a symphony on the radio. After a pause, another hoot, this time joined by calls from several other animals around us. We gazed intently at the nest as the forest grew dimly lighter, still before sunrise. From time to time there was more calling, and we heard the breaking of a branch where a chimp had started feeding to our left. Suddenly I saw Manueri pointing, and there was our chimp, squatting over the edge of his nest for his early morning toilet requirements. Having done which, without a hoot or a look at his abandoned bed, he clambered speedily down his tree, and made off along the forest floor towards the feeding area. No ceremony, no dawdling; having slept the best part of twelve hours, he had woken hungry and hurried off for breakfast.

And what a sight greeted us on the breakfast tree! We edged up slowly to a point where we could see, and found about a dozen chimps, males, females, and youngsters, feeding with tremendous zest on the wild fruits of an ngrube in the understorey. They were stuffing handfuls of food into their mouths, looking around all the time for a new bunch, swinging about, and even squabbling to get at the ripest, yellowest fruit. Everywhere chimps were moving about, feeding and hooting and occasionally squabbling, with wild screams from the loser of the fray. This first hour certainly seemed to be the most active feeding period of their day.

We watched for a while, until we too began feeling desperately hungry. The sun was now well up and the tree-tops were yellow-green. Looking at the guards, I saw that they had tired of watching and were lying on their backs, smoking, while Manueri sat, as he liked to in the forest, in the crotch between two buttresses of a giant tree. They smiled at us, tolerant of our excessive interest in the soko-mutu, but they understood by now that there was no thing in particular we were trying to do, or see, but that we wanted to find out everything about these strange men of the woods, and they were more than pleased when our luck was good and our notebook was crammed with information.

We returned to camp, where a fire was going, fed on sandwiches and tea, and agreed it had been a good morning. The chimps were far away by now, out of earshot. We packed our bags and trudged out of the forest, getting to the Land Rover only to find it had a flat tyre. The wheel nuts had rusted on and would not budge; it was uncomfortably hot and the horse-flies were biting. There was nothing to do but walk home and walk home we did, arriving at midday with sweat pouring from our faces and darkening our jackets. Tit for tat: we had been favoured for a few hours, and then while our spirits were high we had been damned. We now felt, in the midday heat, that Africa was unfriendly and against us and useless to struggle against—we had walked three miles or more with rucksacks on our backs and cameras and things banging against us.

But we had arranged, despite ourselves, to leave again at 5 P.M. After a bath and some lunch I walked back to the Land Rover, lightly clad and armed with a heavy spanner, changed the wheel, and set out looking for a likely group of chimps. The cycle began again.

We kept it up for almost a week, a memorable time in which we gained greater intimacy with the forest and the chimpanzees, got to know the men, and discovered not only how to hang a hammock, but also how the chimpanzee has solved its sleeping problems. The first of these is knowing just when to start thinking seriously of going to bed. There are several signs: the air cools suddenly, cicadas begin their chirping one by one until the air is a merry din, and hornbills wing their rasping way to their roosting trees outside the forest on the slopes of Busingiro or Little Kasenene Hill. All these are indicators of approaching night.

During the last hour or so of daylight, we watched the chimpanzees as they fed briskly, conscious perhaps of the need to have a full stomach on retiring in order to avoid insatiable pangs of hunger at night. Sometimes they looked over the canopy towards the sun, as if to see how the time was running out. Then it flipped behind the hills and, one by one, they left feeding with a last crammed mouthful and made their way out along the branches into another tree, or down the trunk and along the ground.

Now there was some hooting in the still of the evening, as chimpanzees located themselves in their nesting positions, for usually they nested in small groups of three or four, each in sight of the others. Some were already at work, others were selecting a site. A late one was still feeding—perhaps he would not make a nest at all. Site selection was fascinating to watch: one chimp looked up into a sapling, climbed it, climbed down again, went up a bigger tree and out along a branch, and there decided to build. Sitting on the main branch, he pulled in surrounding leafy branches, working his way round in a circle and intertwining the branches, holding them in place beneath his feet. He did not break them off completely but just snapped them half through so that their resilience was gone but they were still firmly attached to the tree. Having used every available branch at the site, he found his nest was still patchy, so he collected more branches from nearby, breaking them off this time, and laid them on top, or wove them in a little, finally adding leafy twiglets to complete the big, firm structure in which he was going to sleep. He did all this in three or four minutes; now followed a settling-down period of from five to ten minutes during which he made final adjustments (from our hidden vantage point below all we could see were vague arms and hands protruding from the rim of the nest and then disappearing into it again), once he called out and was answered by a brief chorus of good-night hoots, musical and melodious, then it was pitch dark and all was still; we stole away to our camp, pretending to be a firefly with our little torch.

Although the nineteenth-century explorer Paul du Chaillu claimed for himself the distinction of being the first to discover that some chimpanzees made nests, the fact that the

African apes made constructions of some sort had been reported long before. Battell, whose account was published in 1613, had said "They sleepe in the trees, and build shelters for the raine," but whether he was writing of the chimpanzee or the gorilla is uncertain. Du Chaillu's later experience seems to have excited him greatly:

> As I was trudging along . . . I happened to look up at a high tree which we were passing, and saw a most singular looking shelter built in its branches. I . . . was told, to my surprise, that this very ingenious nest was built by the *nshiego mbouvé*. . . . I at once saw that I was on the trail of an animal till now unknown to the civilised world. . . . I no longer felt tired, but pushed on with renewed ardour and with increased caution, determined not to rest till I had killed this nest-building ape.

He got one all right, naming it *Troglodytes calvus*, the bald chimpanzee, one of the two new chimpanzee species he thought he had discovered. (He was wrong in this: all his specimens were members of the one species which was already well known.)

As to the question of why chimpanzees make nests, no very definite answer is possible. Battell's idea, that the nest would provide protection from rain, is not wholly erroneous, for although the ape lies on top of its nest and does not crouch underneath it, the very fact of being off the ground keeps its body drier than it would be curled up on the soggy forest floor. But chimps do not need nests to keep them off the ground—they could just sit in the trees. Alas, we cannot ask our subjects why they make their nests, but even if we could they might not know, for their nest-building behaviour has many of the characteristics of an instinct. One thing is certain—that this complex activity must have developed for good reasons. Why should those chimpanzees which do make a nest have an advantage over those which do not? One way of tackling the problem is by comparing chimpanzees with monkeys. Both sleep in the trees and this doubtless provides some protection from that prowling nocturnal enemy, the leopard. But monkeys do not make nests: they generally have "sitting pads"—bony growths at the buttocks—which help them keep in position on branches during the night. Chimpanzees, on the other hand, rarely have these sitting pads although occasionally they do: it may be that they are losing them on account of their nest-building habit. I would suggest that this changeover from sitting pads to nest-making is a result of increasing size. For while a branch is a big object to a monkey, so that it can find a crotch and wedge itself in securely, this is not so for the much larger chimpanzee, which has to keep all one hundred pounds of himself balanced in a tree all night. So he has responded by making himself a supporting structure, well-developed today but doubtless, in bygone times, no more than a rudimentary structure of a few supporting sticks.

The 259 nests we saw were made at all heights, but the commonest height was thirty to forty feet, i.e. fairly low down in the top level of the understorey. There may be several reasons for this. Down low there is less wind and thus less danger that the chimpanzee will be rocked out of its nest during a stormy night. The branches are younger and more pliable and thus make a more springy nest (foam rubber has nothing on some of the nests we tested). And it would be almost impossible for a leopard to attack a chimpanzee nesting in a sapling, for two reasons: if it climbed up the slender trunk it would cause such a lot of movement that it would wake up the chimp, and if it sprang down out of a nearby tree the sapling would just bend under the combined weight of the two animals and both would crash to the ground, probably coming apart in the process. Whereas if a nest is made on a big branch high up in a tree, all these advantages are lost. Nevertheless some nests are made high up in the tree-tops. Fifteen percent of the ones we saw were over ninety feet high, some a good 150 feet high. And the lowest tree nests we saw were ten or twelve feet off the ground.

Nests were made primarily for night-time sleeping, but sometimes they were made for a nap during the day. There were also other occasions when nests were used; for instance, when a chimpanzee was badly scared but dared not flee it looked about for an old nest, or, failing that, made one hurriedly and climbed in, hiding there quietly and completely hidden until the danger was past.

Nests were nearly always in the trees, but here again there were exceptions, for we found two well-constructed nests on the ground. I remember how we came upon the first one: it was in a little forest clearing of broad-leaved grasses, near a group of nests high up in the trees. It was so well-made, all of grass, and so well pressed down that I wondered if we had a lone gorilla wandering in our forest. Manueri was of the opinion that it was made by a chimp mother for her natal bed, but after we had examined it thoroughly for blood-stains we gave up this idea. We then wondered whether it was an old chimpanzee who could not climb very well, or perhaps one that was sick. The second one was made of shrubs and small branches of nearby saplings, a much rougher affair, dreadfully uncomfortable owing to a snapped-off sapling which stuck up right in the middle of it. It was situated at one end of a small tree-bridge over one of the many streams in the Siba—could it be that a chimp had arrived at this spot late one evening, been uneasy about crossing the water on the thin branch, and finally bedded down on the spot to wait for dawn? We would never know, of course, but we liked to speculate in this way as we tramped through the trees, or lay, hammock-bound, in the forest night. But such problems could hardly be expected to enter the head of Okenyi, who continued to snore away the hours of darkness. And during the daytime his thoughts naturally turned to bigger game. On the sixth evening, when I arrived to collect him, he said an elephant had been heard in a compartment of the Biiso block, and I saw in his eyes the excitement of the hunt. That was his life, not chimp-watching. He had accompanied us graciously, and now must return to his own work. I wished him luck; he grinned broadly; we shook hands, grasped thumbs, and shook hands again. There was no more to say, and we parted.

CHAPTER SIX

The Social Life of Chimpanzees

"One of the most remarkable of all the social habits of the chimpanzee, is the *kanjo*, as it is called in the native tongue. The word . . . implies more the idea of 'carnival.' It is believed that more than one family takes part in these festivities." Thus wrote R. L. Garner of these apes in West Africa. He went on to describe how the chimpanzees fashion a drum from damp clay and wait for it to dry. Then "the chimpanzees assemble by night in great numbers, and then the carnival begins. One or two will beat violently on this dry clay, while others jump up and down in a wild grotesque manner. Some of them utter long, rolling sounds, as if trying to sing. When one tires of beating the drum, another relieves him, and the festivities continue in this fashion for hours." Unlikely? Certainly. True? Almost. Apart from the matter of the drum, this account given nearly seventy years ago describes quite well what we heard and saw six times during our stay in the Budongo Forest—only twice, however, at night.

What is this drum, so often reported, and erroneously thought to be made of clay or to be a hollow tree or log known to or carried about by the chimpanzees? The very name of the chimpanzee in Lunyoro, the local language of our area, is "kitera"—from the stem "tera," which means "to beat," and "ki," the impersonal pronoun "it." The chimpanzee is then: "it beats." To a European the sound is remarkably like the boom of a big bass-drum, not at all like the rat-a-tat of little drums, only occasionally like the medium-pitched kettledrum. Quite early on in our study we were able to establish without a shred of doubt that the chimpanzees produced this sound by beating with hands or feet on the plank buttresses of ironwood trees. We later found that some other species were used as well, but the sound, which we could obtain by striking the buttress with the palms of the hands, would not come from all those species of trees which had buttresses, the reason for which I do not know. The best buttresses for drumming, after the "nyakahimbe" (ironwood) tree, are those of the "mumule" and "mpungu" trees. We found it difficult to observe how the chimps drummed, partly because seeing anything on the forest floor was so difficult, but mainly because if they knew we were close at hand they usually either bolted or crept stealthily away. A few times, though, we caught a glimpse of a chimp thudding against a buttress and heard, from close to, not only the boom but the crack of the wood being struck, the same sound as if a non-reverberating surface had been hit. The actual note produced by the buttress as its surface vibrates is the sound which carries through the trees, not the sharp mechanical whack. Its enormous carrying power is a result of the long wavelength of the very low-pitched note, which has greater penetrating power than notes of higher pitch. Most people will have heard a band playing as it goes away down the road, and will know how much longer it is possible to hear the big bass-drum than any other instrument. The chimpanzee has discovered this principle, and the drumming functions, we believe, to enable contact to be maintained between groups of chimpanzees and even individuals scattered widely over vast tracts of forest where, especially at ground level but also in the tree-tops, visual communication is severely restricted, i.e. the chimps just can't see each other.

Drum buttresses of the finest kind (and the chimpanzees evidently know this too) occur where a tree throws out two planks parallel to each other and about six to nine inches apart, making a sort of open box. If you beat on the outside of such a drum box a beautiful crisp resounding note results, and we several times found depressions in the ground by box drums, where a chimpanzee had squatted.

So much for the drum itself, but what of the "carnivals"? Long before Garner was writing, a missionary in Cape Palmas, West Africa, named Thomas Savage was describing to the Boston Natural History Society what he knew of the way of life of chimpanzees. This was in 1844, and he wrote ". . . They occasionally assemble in large numbers in gambols . . . not less than 50 engaged in hooting, screaming and drumming with sticks on old logs." At a later date, in 1931, Henry Nissen, who made the first thorough scientific study of chimpanzees in the wild, wrote: "Although the cries and drumming presaged no danger to human listeners . . . their very intensity was sufficient to inspire something akin to excited wonderment. . . . When drumming and vocalizing were close by, my guides and porters sometimes trembled in spite of themselves."

Manueri called these carnivals "ngoma," which means "drum," or alternatively "dance," the two ideas being merged in Swahili. From the early days at Budongo we were used to hearing wild chimpanzee noises during the night, terrible howling and screaming, and people said that it must be a leopard attacking the chimps. We came to consider this unlikely, although the noise might well have been a display aimed at frightening off a predator. Neither did we believe that the chimpanzees had come down from their nests to dance in the moonlight; the idea just wasn't good "chimp." So we never solved the riddle of the night noises; and when we had gone into the forest and slept with the chimpanzees, they had called a few times only, never in a really noisy chorus.

It was at the start of the igeria season that we suddenly
came face to face with our first daytime ngoma. We were
watching a group of chimpanzees on the fringe of a swampy
river in the Siba and had noticed that a new group was moving in closer from the north, calling and drumming as it came.
There were about a dozen chimpanzees in our group and perhaps the same number again suddenly climbed up into the
igeria trees with the first lot, whereupon *all* of them began
the wildest screaming and hooting, swinging about, running
along branches at top speed, leaping down branch by branch
to the ground, climbing up again, shaking branches wildly,
and occasionally coming up close to each other to meet briefly
and part again, stamping on branches and slapping them, and
behind all this confusion a steady undercurrent of drumming
resounded. I think on this occasion the performance lasted
for fifty-five minutes, but note-taking was quite impossible—
all we could do was stand in awe and say unscientific things
like "Good heavens, look at that one!" It was at times like
this that we felt things about the chimpanzees but had not
yet formulated them in words.

Was this the ngoma, the kanjo, the carnival of the chimps?
Manueri said yes. We suspected it was a greeting display
when two groups met, although we had watched many utterly
uneventful meetings between groups of chimpanzees as big
as these, and knew that there must be other reasons for this
display. Could it be that there was a latent hostility between
the groups, which had to be worked off? We didn't know
enough about either lot to say. When the carnival was over,
however, they all seemed to be feeding very peacefully beside
each other and they all moved off in the same direction. Later on we saw or heard more "carnivals," one of which lasted
all one afternoon and was on again the next morning (and
may have gone on all the intervening night). We found one
factor common to them: groups which had moved closer to
each other slowly and noisily over a long period beforehand

got into this wildly excited state when they finally met. And as time went by and we learnt more about our chimpanzees, we came to the conclusion that the only times when carnivals occurred were when groups from two different regions met and joined, either to feed briefly together or to stay on a common feeding ground for a few days but finally, with a last resurgence of carnival antics, and with each chimp apparently deciding to which group he wanted to belong and several dashing madly between the parting camps, going their separate ways.

Carnivals apart, the most striking thing about chimpanzee life is the utter tedium of it. We soon found, when in the evenings we wrote up the day's observations in our "chimpanzee log" at home, that though we were seeing chimps nearly every day, very little of extreme interest was taking place. We were getting spoiled and fussy. Now that we had mastered the art of finding our quarry, watching was no longer enough; we wanted to probe deeper into the secrets of chimpanzee life.

One of the most fascinating areas of study concerned the chimpanzees' calls. People sometimes ask, "Do chimpanzees have a language?" and it is a difficult question to answer. For while it is certain that they do not have "words" with precise meanings, it is equally certain that there exists a very complex system of communication in chimpanzees, the most exceptional feature of which is the fact that a whole group of chimpanzees will combine time after time each day to produce a communal din which will carry up to two miles and which is answered by any other groups in the vicinity.

But, getting down to details, we first had to learn to distinguish between the different sorts of calls that individual chimps made. When feeding together, we noticed that grunts and little gruff barks were very common—low-pitched and so quiet that one hardly noticed them; somewhat more excited

were the panting barks—low-pitched sounds followed by a
noisy intake of breath—which accompanied movement from
one tree to another. Then there was the very distinctive "waa"
bark—the sudden, sharp, grating, repeated noise, given with
the mouth half open and lips tensed, which meant "danger!"
and was nearly always a result of a chimp seeing us and taking
fright. Another kind of barking was harsh and shrill, but, unlike the alarm call, was given in choruses, and seemed to result from excitement of some kind.

A completely different sort of call, a series of soft moans,
was sometimes all we knew of the presence of a chimpanzee
ahead of us on the forest floor. This was a "worried" sound
produced by just one animal which was suspicious but perhaps unwilling to make a loud noise and give itself away.
Then there were the hoots—panting hoots and long hoots—
the calls which formed the basis of the choruses. These fine,
loud, whooping calls started at low pitch and intensity with
noisy intakes of breath, and then as the chimps got more
and more worked up, they pouted their lips, their calls rising
to a shriek and culminating in a burst of drumming before all
was quiet and feeding resumed again. Screams and squeals
were given by frightened chimpanzees engaged in quarrels
with one another, and together with howls, roars, and growls,
this made up the spectrum of their conversation.

Naturally, it took time before we could distinguish the
various types of call, especially as the same call, coming from
different animals, had a different tonal quality each time.
Also, quite often, various chimps engaged in different sorts of
calls at one and the same time, and it was hard to sort out
the resultant medley of voices. We made tape recordings and
analysed these in the evenings to try and sort out the more
complicated passages, playing them over and over again. And
we practised imitating the different calls, but somehow our
human voices were too musical, not harsh or windy enough
to get the real chimp tone. We tried calling to the chimps in

the forest, but they never replied, even to a grand chorus of panting hoots given at full blast by Frankie, Manueri, and me. We just were not sufficiently "chimp." However, we did achieve some success by drumming—at least I think we did —for sometimes they seemed to call back or even drum in reply; but then, of course, we could never be sure they wouldn't have done so anyway.

Despite the amazing variety of their calls, we obtained no evidence that chimpanzees communicated complex ideas to one another. The feeding grunts and gruff barks perhaps expressed a feeling of togetherness, for they were not given by a chimpanzee on its own. The "waa" bark was an alarm signal, and other animals found out where the source of danger was by looking to see where the first chimp was staring. The hooting calls seemed to be an expression of excitement caused by the presence of plenty of food, and also by the coming together of a large number of chimpanzees. Screams and squeals expressed fear and directed the attention of nearby chimps to any group member who was having some sort of trouble. So it can be seen that each kind of call or intonation expressed some feeling or other within the animal, and had certain effects on other animals. In humans, this level of communication is found in such behaviour as laughter or crying. Our use of words which have to be learnt, and are specific to particular cultures, is altogether lacking in chimpanzees. Perhaps differences exist between the vocalisations of chimps in one area and those in another—we do not as yet know. If they do, it will make a fascinating subject for study. But however great or slight they may turn out to be, the fact will remain that in its ability to express ideas to its fellows, the chimpanzee has remained very much at the same stage as has been reached by its fellow apes and by the monkeys: despite its undoubted intelligence and ability to learn, it fails at the test of speech.

It has long been known that the vocal organs of chimpanzees do not differ markedly from those of man, and so the "failure" of chimpanzees to learn speech has been attributed to some mental inadequacy. This may or may not be so—we do not know. But expert analysis of our recordings, using sonograms made from our tapes, showed that the structure of the sounds chimpanzees produce is in some ways very similar to the structure of human sounds. For just as humans achieve a variety of effects by varying the pitch of the voice, so do chimpanzees; in short, intonation is the key to the differences between one sound and another in both humans and chimpanzees.

Enough on the subject of calls. For the rest, chimpanzee life seemed a serious, rather tedious business, concerned with finding enough of whichever small, astringent fruits happened to be in season, to fill a stomach the size of a man's, and provide as much energy each day as that required by a long-distance runner! For the chimps, even when they could have stayed all day in one ripe fruit tree, were always moving on to a new feeding place. Rarely were more than two hours spent on any one tree. We soon came to know when they were getting ready to move on. Gradually the chimps in the tree became restless. Some swung about for a few minutes, or stamped their feet on the trunk and gave a few low hoots, then resumed feeding quietly. Often calls were coming in from another group feeding up to a mile away. Our chimps stopped feeding and listened, turning to look in the direction of the calls. Then they answered, and began to move about in the tree. Then, typically, one made up his mind and hurriedly descended. At the base of the tree he grasped a sapling and bent it, swishing it to and fro, before pelting off along a chimp track. The others in the tree looked down. Another one or two left. The first to leave now drummed a few hundred yards ahead, and those left in the tree called in chorus, stuffed a few last fruits in their mouths, and finally left too.

If the chimps continued to call on the way to, and upon arrival at, their new place, then we were able to re-locate them again in an hour or so. But often we bashed on for hours, with the chimps constantly moving further away, always tantalisingly a few hundred yards away. What happened in these cases was that after a few hours feeding in the early morning on a fruiting tree, they were spending many of the middle hours of the day foraging on the forest floor, among low bushes or in the swamp rattans, or eating the fleshy stems of the long green succulent plants which grow wherever enough sunlight peeps through the canopy to supply their broad leaves. When foraging thus, the groups were dispersed and often quiet except for occasional soft gruff barks or squabbling squeals. We could never see through the dark denseness of undergrowth inside the forest, and in this way many a day came to a disappointing end. But the chimps usually had a routine which they kept up for a number of days at a time, and sure enough, next morning, back they were on the previous day's fruit tree. Sometimes when most had moved off in the mid-morning, an ageing granddad, with greying hair and a bald patch on his lower back, would remain behind, gazing out over his domain. Or on other occasions, one or two mothers with their youngsters stayed in the tree, lazily feeding or just staring, apparently unmoved by the excitement which gripped those about to leave.

But what of the social life, the interactions between one chimp and another? Often we watched a party of chimps for hours before any social interaction took place; they were too busy feeding or just sat looking out over the trees and scratching themselves with long sweeps of the hand across the body. There was no burning desire to get together. And then one of them would make his way in desultory fashion (Antonioni's characters have nothing on chimps) towards another, sit beside it, and start grooming, or, to use less jargon, back-scratching it. This was the most usual form of social behaviour, and usually occurred when a small number of chimpanzees had settled down peacefully in a comfortable tree after an in-

tense and satisfying bout of feeding, before the call came
to move on to a new place. In the periods when fruit was
scarce there was so much moving about from place to place
that there seemed little time for such relaxed social activities.
But when, in the fig season for example, stomachs were vis-
ibly bulging around mid-morning, a general wave of sociability
would sweep through the group, and soon the animals would
be in little knots grooming each other. As in gorillas and many
species of monkeys, the females were the busiest groomers.
Several females with their young often huddled together all
grooming each other. On one occasion we spent hours watching two females in a tree. One was an adolescent and the
other was very, very old—so old that her head was bald, her
cheeks sunken, her movements slow and laboured. She may
have been over thirty, which is old for a chimp. The young
one followed her, slowly, wherever she went, as if devoted to
her, and every now and then groomed her. Finally grandma
made herself a nest and sank down to rest in it, at which the
young one left her to feed on nearby branches.

Adult males occasionally groomed each other, but most
often females groomed males. One day we watched a female
who was very much in demand. There were four chimps in a
tree, one female and three adult males. At first they were just
feeding. Then one male came along a branch towards the female and sat down with his back to her, obviously suggesting
to her that she might groom him. The female who was thus
presented with a back, obligingly scratched it for a while,
selecting one little spot and carefully examining every square
centimetre of it, parting the hairs, and sometimes removing
bits of dirt, loose hairs, or anything else she found there.
Meanwhile number-one male closed his eyes in drowsy ecstasy—I knew exactly how he felt, as Frankie is an expert
back-scratcher—but, I wondered, how does a non-talking
chimp direct the attention of his partner to that persistent
little itch just to the left of the spine a little way below the

shoulder-blade? As I wondered, male number one shifted his position drowsily, stretching his neck backwards until the top of his head was presented to the good-natured female. Ah— so he wanted a head scratch now. But just at this moment male number two came down from a branch above where he had been feeding, and, approaching the grooming couple, he sat down behind the female and started grooming her. This went on for some time, and then the good-natured female turned round to groom male number two, perhaps knowing full well that this was what he wanted all the time, and his unselfish gesture was just a way of getting her to notice him. Meanwhile male number three was feeding and watching the threesome below him. Suddenly male number three swung down towards the grooming group, which immediately split up, and then we saw that the good-natured female was grooming male number three! Was he a more important customer than the other two?

The peace of the afternoon was eventually broken by calls coming over the trees from a neighbouring group, and all the males became alert and swung off one by one out of the tree. We were amused to watch our good-natured female lie down now, stretch out on the branch on one side, head on hand, shut her eyes, and go to sleep; her work for the afternoon was completed.

We found that sexual relationships among wild chimpanzees were casual and easy-going, in contrast with, say, wild baboons, where the most powerful adult male has the right to a female in heat, even though she may mate with other males before and after the peak of her cycle, and also in contrast with chimpanzees living in captivity, which often develop passions and jealousies that do not show themselves in the wild.

With chimpanzees, when the female comes into estrus, which means she is in heat, and sexually receptive to the male, she swells up behind a glorious pink colour, displaying her private parts with such gusto that we used this end of her, rather than her face, for temporary identification purposes. This happens every five weeks, on average, lasting for about a week at a time. During the rest of her cycle, the female is uninteresting to the male, and presumably not interested in him. I remember Frankie remarking on one occasion that she thought this "one week on, four off" shift system was rather a good way of arranging things. For one thing, she said, a girl would have a whale of a time being tremendously popular on her week on, and the four weeks off would give her a wonderful chance to have a rest and get on with her work; gone would be the desperate need for women to keep competing with each other all the time.

One day we were lucky enough to watch the whole mating procedure in ideal conditions of observation. A neat, blackhaired young female with a big rounded pink bottom was standing still on a branch, her behind pointing towards an adult male sitting very close by in a tree crotch. The male kept eyeing the female from time to time. Then slowly grasping the branch above, but without really moving his position, he mated with her for a few seconds, then sat back and looked around. This was repeated twice more, then the male started grooming the female. All this time a young three-year-old, perhaps the offspring of the female, was watching from a branch above. After a while the male lay down and curled up to sleep in his tree crotch, but the female wanted his constant attention, and soon he had to rouse himself and groom her again. A few minutes later another suitor moved into the picture, a smaller adult male, obviously attracted by the same female. Male number two now also started grooming the female, so both males were courting her. What happened next was as delicate a piece of manoeuvring as anything in *Jules and Jim*. The female moved to present her behind to the second male and he made as if to mount her, but then male number one suddenly *started to groom him*. Male number two sat down again, distracted, and both males now engaged in mutual grooming, ignoring the poor desirous female! However, when she decided to leave the tree, both males followed her, male number one going first. Though we did not see the end of this story, it seems likely that male number two would in fact have his chance later, but that for the moment, male number one was chief consort.

On another occasion when we observed jungle love-making, the receptive female was in a tree with no less than four adult males. After one finished mating with her, he moved away, and another moved close to pay his attentions. However, not always was a female in heat surrounded by a retinue. Once we saw a rosy-blushing female presenting to a male who was trying to get a good meal, and every time she closed in he simply walked away.

In marked contrast with what goes on when chimps are forced to live cooped up in small cages, we never saw homosexual or auto-erotic behaviour in our wild animals.

From the amount of noise the chimps made (twenty or thirty loud choruses a day were quite common), one would have thought that they were a very quarrelsome breed, but in fact quarrels were uncommon. One reason for this could well be that there was so much *space* in the forest that if one chimp did not like another he could easily avoid him without coming to blows. Again we have here a difference from baboon society, where all members of a troop remain permanently within sight of some of the others, and the dominant males exert their authority to maintain a proper deference to age and direct the group's movements over the feeding grounds. Chimpanzee society seemed to have none of this. Chimps seemed to treat one another more as individuals, and their relationships were perhaps more those of personal likes and dislikes than is the case in baboons. There were certainly important, powerful adult males. Thus, in the example given above of grooming behaviour, two adult males moved away when a third came to present for grooming to the female. On another occasion, we saw a small thin adult male literally fall off a branch onto the one below as a large powerful adult male came striding along. But the big difference between chimpanzees and baboons was that in the chimps there were no permanent groups for the forceful, fully mature males to lead.

This did not mean, however, that they never took over leadership functions temporarily—they very often did. For instance, when a group had been feeding in a tree, climbing around and up and down and with odd members going and others arriving, it was not until a big male descended the tree and let out a big "boom-boom" on a buttress that the others *all* decided to go with him and hurriedly left the tree. Once, too, a big male was in the lead of a party of seventeen chimpanzees crossing the main road. After they had crossed he went back to the side they had come from for a minute, then re-crossed and the whole lot went hooting and drumming into the forest—had he been checking up to see if anyone was still to come, a hesitant chimp, perhaps, too shy to cross the road near where we were standing? And then there was a group of four adult males we came to know quite well, big, confident, and often curious, coming towards us in a relaxed and dignified manner for a closer inspection—a kind of royal clan. But mostly it was the opposite—suspicious, shy chimpanzees that made their way through the forest without leaders, and left trees in twos and threes as the mood took them, so that we never knew what to expect. Even mothers and their infants sometimes strayed alone—I remember one occasion when I was sitting well hidden in shrubs beside a chimpanzee track waiting for a call; a mother walked right past me less than a yard away, her infant sitting up jockey style on her back. Another time Manueri went off "choo"; suddenly I heard a shout but left him to sort it out, and when he returned I gathered that he had been quietly performing his function when a mother in a hurry had almost run into him, the baby had fallen off and he had tried to grab it but being rather immobile with his trousers down had failed and the mother had retrieved it before dashing off. The whole thing had amused him immensely.

I was glad that he had not succeeded in catching the baby. It is fun, no doubt, to have a pet chimp around the house, and we would have had no space problems. The little creature and its mother would have been sad at first, and so would we for them, but we would all have got over it. Time would go by and there would be jolly antics on Busingiro Hill—and then? We could not keep a growing chimp in our small London flat. He would have to go away. He probably could not be returned to the forest as he would have grown too attached to humans, and to us in particular; and if we really were determined to set him free this might be a long process, as Barbara Harrisson has discovered with her orang-utans. Almost certainly it could not be done cleanly and quickly at a time determined by our departure. There might be a good home somewhere, but he would go on growing and would reach the stage all too quickly when he didn't know his own strength. Then a steel cage would be found for him, and in it he would spend the whole of his maturity, the whole of these wonderful Budongo years of meetings and explorations and carnivals and stormy nights under the tree-tops. Too great a sacrifice, surely, for a few months of fun and games. I told Manueri, as I had before, that we wanted no pet chimps.

Just occasionally, two chimps started to quarrel. These were usually short scuffles in which the animals either actually fought or one threatened the other by means of barks and branch-shaking while the victim screamed long and loud in a high-pitched piercing voice. From the screams alone one would have thought that one of them was being murdered, but it was generally no more than a tiff over a bunch of fruit. When a real fight started in a tree all one could see was a tangled mass of arms and legs struggling together among the leaves, but since both animals had to hang on for dear life with at least one hand, their freedom was curtailed, and after a few seconds one dived down onto a lower branch screaming and looking up at the victor with mixed fear and hate in its eyes. Within ten minutes the two of them might be feeding quite happily beside each other again.

Big males rarely came to blows. I remember one morning (it was one of the mornings when we had spent the night in the forest) we were watching a big male *feeding from his nest*—he had sited it beautifully the night before, right among several enormous clusters of lovely ripe yellow ngrube fruits. So he sat breakfasting in bed like a film star and all he needed was a maroon silk dressing gown and a copy of the *Times* brought in by a butler on a silver tray. But instead, a male of about his own size came up along a branch, reached the nest, pushed him rudely with a hand, at which he resisted, pushed again, and he meekly got up and left it, threatening the new-comer from behind his back with a couple of jerks, and then shambling miserably away.

One day, a chimp decided to quarrel with us! It was in June, and we were in the Siba swamp-forest, closing in on some chimps, which were about a hundred yards away in the tree-tops. We were standing near a big tree with a thick liana snaking down from it. Manueri climbed onto a bend in the liana and looked towards the chimps to try and locate them. He jumped down and his feet thumped on the ground. "Wewe soko-mutu," I said—"You are a chimp." He laughed. We edged forward and had scarcely gone a couple of paces when we heard movements ahead on the ground. We froze to watch whatever was coming our way. At that moment a big adult male broke cover and came for us in a slight curve. He was a big chimp, his head was sunk deep on his shoulders, his eyes were cast down, and his mouth was shut in a scowl. He was galloping silently towards us in leaps and I felt certain he was going to attack. Manueri immediately took a step towards him and slashed about with his panga, hissing. I shouted and raised the camera tripod I was carrying, ready to bring it down on his head. He turned in his tracks and ran back into the bushes out of sight. Later on, I was to be charged by an adult male gorilla, and learn how much more terrifying that can be, but this experience with the chimpanzee was a shock. We measured the distance to the spot where he had churned the earth up in his turning—it was three paces from where we had stood.

Two days later, in the very same area, we had another surprise—this time we met a bad-tempered old lady. Once again we were creeping up to a group feeding about seventy yards ahead, where we could hear the rustling of branches and the gruff barks of a party of chimpanzees. There was a noise in the undergrowth close by to our right, and at the same time a chimp baby started screaming a short way up a tree very close by. We turned and suddenly an old female rushed out of cover, with lowered brows and mouth half open, eyes fixed on us, and charged straight towards us. Again we prepared to defend ourselves. The chimp stopped, glowered at us from five yards, then just as suddenly as she had appeared, rushed back up the tree to collect the toto, and ran off with it across a tree-bridge over the Siba River and into the trees. This was the only time we knew of when a female behaved in such a way. Perhaps when she saw us she was separated from her baby and wanted to bluff us so as to give herself time to retrieve it. We admired both her courage and the sensible way she had left baby behind when running against the foe. But Manueri shook his head and said, "A-a, if we come here to these wild Siba chimps too often we shall definitely be bitten; 'Siba kali sana' [the Siba is very wild]." So we left them alone for a couple of weeks; anyway, we told ourselves, they were a rotten lot of chimps, and they lived in a dismal swamp.

These were two of the very few moments when there was

ever any question that a chimp might attack us. With gorillas, which, like chimps, are normally harmless creatures unless
provoked, the advice, if you are charged, is to stand still and
calm, facing the animal, when it will stop. This requires courage—more, as it turned out, than we ourselves had. But with
chimps I would not give that advice. I think it is better to
step forwards, shout, and threaten back if things get too hot.

CHAPTER SEVEN

Africans of Budongo

If you look at Plate 19 (air photo No. 51/ug/6.017 of the Department of Lands and Surveys, Uganda), you will see on it a section of the southern rim of the Budongo Forest. At first the photograph will strike you as being extremely monotonous, showing as it does a sea of trees over most of the area, with tentacles of forest probing out southwards at the bottom. Then your eye will be drawn to a little bare patch in the trees near the centre of the map, and looking carefully you will see thread-like lines running to and from it. This patch is the site of Budongo Sawmills Ltd., the largest sawmill in Uganda, and the threads are, of course, roads.

Coming down to earth, and standing in the middle of that same triangle, the picture is very different. For man is midget-sized in comparison with the vast area he has cleared and, standing in the middle of the mill, it is easy to forget completely the surrounding miles of trees. Let us look around more closely. Entering from the south, we pass the labour lines to our left—white, well-built huts in which the loggers and sawyers live with their families—and come to the mill duka—which sells maize meal, beans, cigarettes, salt, tea in tiny packets, native cloth, exercise books, and pencils and a variety of other things such as Tembo coffee, locally grown and two shillings (28 cents) a pound. The duka has a verandah which is covered with dirty children. Opposite is a huge timber store, roofed over, with hundreds of planks stacked neatly in criss-cross pattern to air. Further up is the dispensary—a local first-aid unit run entirely by the mill for its staff. If this sounds commonplace, consider that here, totally unsung, is an outpost akin to that splendid achievement of Great Britain, the National Health Service, for the men and women who receive treatment here pay nothing—the dispensary is subsidised by the mill. It is run by a beaming African who always wears a green sweater—his methods of treatment vary according to the man in front of him. He knows the lazy-bones, and his response to people who have not clearly got some specific disease or injury is generally scorn. I remember one occasion when Manueri appeared on a Monday morning nursing a very bad leg and swollen knee. Fearing a dislocation I took him to the dispensary, where this man gave him a whack on the back and told him to drink less "waragi" and then he wouldn't fall over. It was the best thing he could have done and Manueri was soon perfectly all right again. Had the dispenser sympathised and felt the tender knee and bandaged it up Manueri would have retired to bed for a week or two genuinely believing himself unable to work.

Opposite the dispensary and a bit further along the road was the petrol pump. This was of immense value to us since the Land Rover required constant refuelling and the nearest commercial pump was seventeen miles away, while here at the mill we were a mere seven miles from home. Robin Knight, the manager of the mill, had kindly given us permission to use the mill's facilities and so there I was, in the heart of Africa, with no more to do than sign my name on the bill for a full tank, and pay later. The existence of the mill had, of course, been a factor in deciding us to work in the Budongo Forest in the first place. But we could not help feeling favoured in comparison with those early explorers of a hundred or even fifty years ago, trudging exhausted through the elephant grass, unable to conceive of life as we could now enjoy it.

And we were not isolated like those early pioneers. The mill had a telephone link with Masindi and operated a daily mail service to and from the Masindi post office. Letters from home arrived at the mill within a week and then it was simply a matter of time until we came up and collected them. We felt we were in contact with the outside world, and it was a comforting thought. The mill's nerve centre, from which these facilities operated, was a single raised wooden building with a verandah and a Union Jack (replaced in October by the Uganda flag with its crested crane) hanging from a tall flagpole outside. There were four rooms: on the left Robin Knight's office, then mill engineer David Kershaw's, then assistant manager George Barrow's, and lastly the general office in which numerous African and Asian clerks sat at desks. It was a pleasant building with a busy atmosphere and could have been the headquarters of any big commercial undertaking anywhere, except that now and again the crash of a lorry emerging from the forest with a felled giant, and the steady beating of the overhead sun, reminded one of where one was.

The mill itself, with its giant ten-inch bandsaws perpetually screaming, was a huge building open at both ends, to the left from the office steps. The scene inside was hugely impressive. A hundred Africans, of the four hundred employed by the mill, moved about their tasks, some high up in the rafters, bringing the enormous trees into alignment with the blades, moving them relentlessly forwards, backwards, an inch to the left, then forwards again until the first clean slice had been removed from the trunk, part of the six hundred tons of sawn timber produced each month. The din was immense; two or three saws worked at once and Africans shouted to each other; cut planks were piled and prepared for the smaller circular saws at the far end of the building where the edges were trimmed, removing the bark and bringing the planks to standard widths; the useless timber was thrown out onto huge heaps of firewood which was then collected for the mill's boilers, and by other firms and individuals—including ourselves —for household uses. A background symphony to all this was the roar of the generators in the adjoining building. Driven by steam from huge boilers, they greedily consumed vast quantities of wood fuel, producing electricity for the whole mill, including the 100-horsepower motors which drove the saws. And on top of all this, in the same building, was Bob Angus's vehicle-repair department, with trucks being dismantled and engines being tuned, the sharp heavy clatter of steel on steel and a hundred shouted orders and questions and jokes flying through the air.

One could do little but stand and stare. These African men knew the part they played, and worked with precision. They clearly enjoyed the power of working with heavy equipment, the heaviest of its kind in all Uganda. They were the lucky few, the 5 percent with jobs in this underemployed kingdom of Bunyoro: a motley bunch of tough migrant labourers. Their home lives had been disrupted and the control of tradition over their behaviour was weak. They could be called the first victims in this area of industrialisation. They were toughened from hard work and living among strangers in a strange country. But they had money, and freedom to do what they liked with it, the prestige of the wage-earner over his family and friends who work the earth and are tied to one spot forever.

One thing this money brought them was meat. Every Saturday a little group of cattle, lean and heavy-horned, could be seen making its way up the track towards the mill under the guardianship of a couple of equally skinny herdsmen. Believe it or not, this party was in the process of finishing a 150-mile trek on foot from the north. Poor cattle! It was well for them they did not know that their long and tiring journey led to the slaughter-house; perhaps they imagined some sweet grassy plain on the banks of a crystal river in which they would slake their thirst. Arrived at the mill they were instantly despatched and then cut up with a hatchet by the mill's "butcher." As work ended at noon on Saturday and word got about that the meat had arrived, a huge queue formed outside the butcher's "shop," a wire-mesh enclosure, and each man (ourselves included) took away his share of the spoils, until everything was gone and even the huge heaps of guts had disappeared. This meat was known locally as "Budongo beef." It had to be well cooked owing to the numerous inhabitants of those West Nile cattle; and since they had lived a lifetime at bare subsistence level, and were hardier than cattle in more favourable climes anyway, the resulting beef was extraordinarily tough—outmatched only, in my experience, by elephant meat. Sinews seemed to be the rule rather than the exception and at times we might as well have been eating our shoes. Frequently we were forced to abandon supper on account of jaw-ache. What nutritive value there was in that meat I cannot imagine, but it was amazing how avidly everyone bought it and ate it, how we Europeans and the Indians and the Africans all shared a desperate desire for meat. Man, I was left in little doubt, is a natural carnivore.

Pay-day came on the first Saturday of the month, and that was when the revels really began. For few of these Africans saved their money; they feared thieves, and had, for the most part, no long-term projects which required savings. Most men spent their wages quickly on clothes, food, and drink, the proportion allocated to each varying from man to man. On pay-day Saturday mornings a constant stream of women could be seen making their way up the road towards the mill. Some had children with them, all had heavy loads on their heads. They were carrying their produce as far as ten miles to sell it at the mill's Saturday market: sweet potatoes and maize and tomatoes and avocados, and passion fruit and guavas and

melons and bananas. Men could also be seen now, with large
gourds strapped to the panniers of their bicycles—each gourd
containing over a gallon of thick grey native beer. Everyone
was happy in an abandoned way; after a month of frustrations
in which there was never enough money for anything, the end
of the month had come and money was a-plenty.

Down at the main road the impetus of the infection is felt
too, and here towards the middle of the afternoon a drum
begins to beat a steady boom-boom which will go on into
the night. Small groups of men and women stand in the sun
talking; they wear smiles. Girls begin to appear, neatly dressed
and with their hair done carefully. Young men, too, walk
about confidently in the best clothes they can muster. They
go back into the square yard where the drum is beating out
its message and join the others dancing on the bare earth floor.
It is not a dance with steps but a Congo dance. They shift
their feet a little but rapidly, and let their bodies twist and
lean, losing the rhythm and gaining it again, breaking off for
a draught of local beer from the big central bowl or drinking
it from a friend's gourd while dancing. Women turn their
backs and wiggle their bottoms provocatively, the men re-
spond with shouts and jumps, the drum is joined by a guitar
and some adapted bicycle pumps. The afternoon light is failing, some are already leaving with their friends to stroll homewards through the tropical dusk; the rest drink and talk and
dance on.

But down in the forest behind the huts, there is something
sinister going on. Half a mile into the trees, in a spot known
only to a hard-core few, under a giant fig tree, "waragi" is being consumed in earnest. Waragi, double distilled from beer,
is colourless, aphrodisiac, and enormously intoxicating. Waragi is illegal, and a man will go to prison for up to three years
if he is found making it. Distilled in swamps and other inaccessible places with the use of copper tubing, waragi sells at three
shillings, or forty-two cents, a bottle among men who know

they can trust each other: men who are addicted. Manueri, I regret to say, was one such. Not that he ever distilled the stuff or even knew where this took place, nor even that he *had* to drink it every now and again. But if he had the money, he spent it on waragi, rather than clothes or meat, which I never knew him to buy. He could drink two bottles and be all right next day; three bottles and he had to stay in bed. Normal men lose all self-control after a single bottle.

The trouble with waragi, we were told, and the reason it is illegal, is that not only is it a dangerously strong spirit, but owing to the poisons in it, it too often has the long-term effect of making men insane or actually killing them. If it were properly distilled this would not occur, and thus there is an argument for the whole waragi business being brought into the open. But if this did occur the amount of drunkenness and alcoholism might increase enormously. Africans told me it was unfair that Europeans should be allowed to buy whisky (prohibitively expensive for themselves) while they were not allowed to buy waragi, and I could not answer them that whisky has no ill-effects on the drinker for that is patently untrue. Nor could I say that whisky being more expensive than waragi, Europeans drink less as a result, for in comparison with his earning power a bottle of whisky costs a European no more than a bottle of waragi costs an African, and there is no doubt that some white men drink far more than is good for them. The Africans certainly had a point. But at the same time, it was clear that waragi would have to be kept fairly scarce. Since independence, the Uganda government has made a major change in the waragi laws. A new central distillery has been built near Kampala, to produce a predetermined quantity of "legal" waragi, for distribution and sale under licence all over the country. All private production of waragi will remain illegal. Whether this legal waragi will reach those who need it, and whether the new distillery will eliminate the need for private stills, or co-exist with them, remains to be seen. Certainly it will not be possible to reduce the total waragi consumption. And I would not, myself, want to take away this fiendish pleasure from such poor people whose lives have little enough excitement. Not all of them go raving mad. Manueri may have been beastly when he was drunk, but sober he had a depth of personality which is rare in more inhibited folk. Despite, or perhaps because of, his monthly transgressions of the liquor laws, he had a wisdom of which I would be proud.

When Okenyi goes out to hunt for elephant, he leaves before dawn. Waking instinctively half an hour before the black sky turns red and the hyraxes stop their calling, he pulls on his khaki sweater with GAME written on it in big red letters at the front, pulls on his shorts, winds khaki puttees around his legs starting under the foot and ending below the knee, laces his heavy boots, then feels for his rifle. He checks his ammunition, buttons his bush-jacket, and is gone. If you come looking for Okenyi at dawn, his hut is already empty.

This is when he goes out alone, to hunt through the day and return at nightfall. It is different when he stays out longer, for then he goes accompanied by his fellow game guard, Okello, and each of them has a porter to carry food and a blanket. In that way they can stay out for days. But I think Okenyi prefers to hunt alone; his skill outmatches his friend's, he sees more, and moves more silently.

Marco Okenyi is an Acholi, a hunter by training and a game guard by profession. He is tall, some six feet or more, and slim; his eyes are sharp and intelligent, and his wit is instantaneous. The local Africans gather round him: he is a natural leader. They respect him because he is a killer of many elephants, they keep friends with him because he gives them meat, they laugh with him because he is companionable, they get drunk with him because he has money for beer. Okenyi also has money for wives, and at present he has four. The first was a church wedding, for Marco is a Catholic. The rest were

common-law weddings, without fuss and bother—a payment
to the girl's father, with money-back guarantee if she was un-
satisfactory. Marco has between ten and twenty children—it
is impossible to count them all. He probably knows how many
there are, but I forgot to ask him.

As he walks along the track a faint greyness is already ap-
pearing in the sky through the leaves, but below in the forest
the blackness of night persists. A late hyrax roars in a tree
above him, its raucous growl rising with each burst to a fren-
zied pitch, as if survival depended on it. A mile inside the forest dawn is reaching the forest floor as Okenyi watches a
leopard, a leopard he knows well and which knows him and
knows it is safe from the gun. Twitching its tail, the leopard
watches the man pass by from its resting place in the low
branch of a tree and watches him disappear round a far bend
before resting its head on its paws again. Next, Okenyi comes
upon a flock of guinea-fowl feeding on the track ahead of him,
thirty of them at least, each one a tasty, filling supper of delicious tender white meat. But what can he do? With his big
.404 he would disintegrate a bird completely. On top of which
his rounds are accountable to the Game Department. And
finally he doesn't want to make a noise, for two reasons:
firstly he doesn't want to scare off any elephants that may
be around, and secondly he is still close to camp—if he shot
they would hear it and start speculating. All this he wants to
avoid. But how ridiculously unaware of him the guinea-fowl
are! He walks right up to them in the dim misty morning,
wishing he had a bow and arrow—anything but this huge ele-
phant-stopper in his hand. They scatter finally to right and
left and some flap up into the trees, the green-blue gloss of
their spotted feathers glinting in the first rays of sunlight
near the tops of the trees.

Okenyi walks on, his tread as regular as a clock, his senses
and his mind open, absorbing every detail of the scene around
him. An elephant-shrew trots onto the track ahead of him

and he stops to watch. "Sasa tembo" they say in Swahili, with
a grin—"like an elephant." The name is a joke; if you ask people what it is called they always say "sasa tembo" and grin.
The shrew sniffs the air; Okenyi is a tree-stump. It scratches
its cheek with a hind foot. It has big, mobile ears. It is not at
first sight like a shrew: far too big, eight inches long with a
few more inches of tail, but its nose is elongated, shrew-fash-
ion, into a proboscis, and hence the name. It trots on, into
the forest.

It is light now and Okenyi begins a cigarette. He has
crossed two bridges and he is about two miles into the forest
as the hornbill flies. He leaves the main track and follows a
Forest Department boundary marking the border-line between
two "compartments" of forest which have been tended since
felling thirty years ago, to ensure a good crop of timber trees.
Okenyi's job is to see that elephants are kept out of these
compartments, for elephants are the greatest menace to silvi-
culture here, with their passion for the delicate taste of the
mahogany sapling. He is now walking between two compartments on a boundary that runs as straight as an arrow from
east to west, as far as the forest edge. Every now and then a
mass of undergrowth around a fallen tree has to be negotiated,
but he knows all of these spots and the tracks around them:
little notches on the trees guide him. Old buffalo prints, and
the prints of pigs and antelopes do not interest him beyond a
brief examination: these too he knows individually, even
the time when they first appeared. Monkeys leap away as he
passes, or sit with jerky head movements spluttering and chir-
ruping as they watch him.

Finally he reaches the spot where, yesterday, Forest Department workmen heard an elephant browsing, waiting just
long enough to make sure it was not a buffalo before they
fled. Okenyi knows the exact spot, for it was described to him
at length the evening before. Tree by tree in their minds,
Okenyi and the Forest Department men came to this very

[9] At its base the ironwood tree throws out plank buttresses. These are the chimpanzees' favorite drum. By beating on the side of a buttress with hands or feet, a chimpanzee can produce a deep, penetrating note like that of a bass drum, and this sound can carry up to two miles in the forest.

[10] On our very first day in the Budongo Forest we were accompanied by Marco Okenyi, the elephant-hunter (second from left), and two men from the nearby village of Dwoli.

[11] The author, with the Budongo Forest in the background.

[12] Manueri.

[13] Home after the rain: myself, Frankie, and Manueri.

[14] "Watu Hapana" built himself a little shelter by the road-side, from which he did his chimp-spotting for us.

[15] From ground level, the Budongo sawmill looks busy and industrial, and it is easy to forget the miles of surrounding trees.

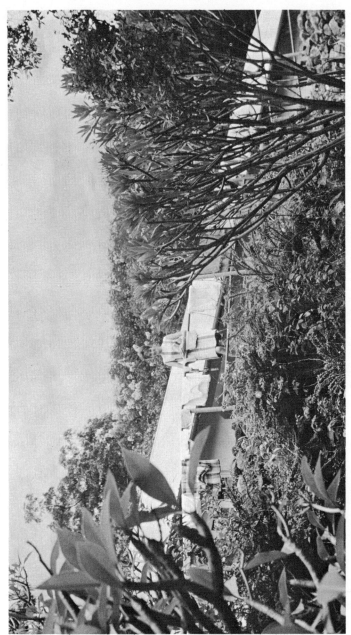

[16] Frankie, our house on the hill, our flower-decked garden, and the washing.

[17] Dawn over Budongo.

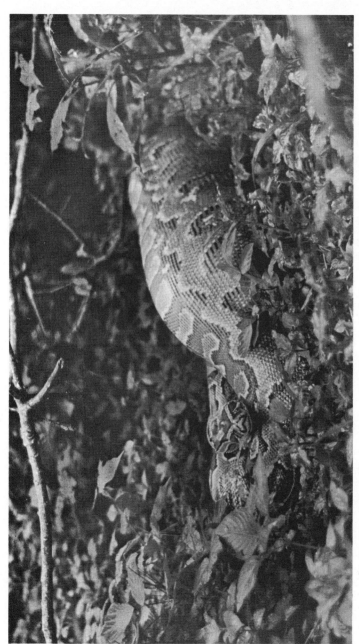

[18] The python kept its eyes fixed on us. It had swallowed a large duiker and was unable to move away.

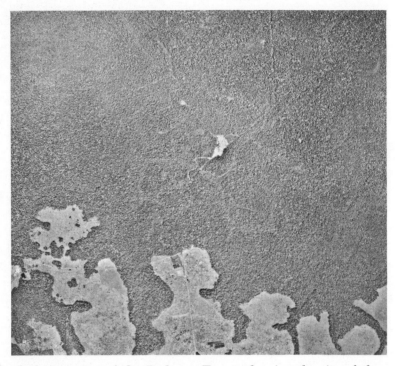

[19] A section of the Budongo Forest, showing the site of the sawmill (near center) and roads.

spot; there could be no mistake between men who knew the forest so well. Okenyi now knows that he has to go three hundred paces to the north in order to reach the spot where the elephant was heard, and he also knows that it will not be there now. So first he walks on up the track to see if it has crossed. It has not. Returning to the spot he enters the forest. Counting his steps he heads north, following the track of the Forest Department men. He reaches the place where they were working: some of the trees are newly ringed. A knife has been dropped in the hurry to leave; he thinks how useful it might be, shoulders his rifle by the strap, then decides against the knife and walks on carefully. He can already smell the dung. He reaches it.

Now Okenyi has to think hard. He puts down his gun and stands by the dung and looks at it. Standing on every side of the dung he looks up, slowly, noticing the pattern of broken branches and crushed leaves. The elephant's track is clear and he walks up it, first one way and then the other. A branch lies fallen across the track; on one side it is grazed and the white wood shows through. He squats to examine the graze. The skin of the branch has been pulled upwards. It is all he needs to know. This damage can only be the result of a foot being lifted over the branch and so he knows which way tembo, the elephant, was going. Shouldering his weapon, Okenyi starts to follow the track. He is in no hurry, nor is he unduly careful in his movements: the dung is a day old. Judging from the size of the prints the beast is medium large, but something distresses Okenyi: he finds that while some of the prints are deep and regular (the depth being due not only to the weight of the animal but to the fact that it places its hind foot in the depression made by the forefoot), each alternate print is skewed strangely to one side, and a groove in front of the print shows that one foot is not picked up cleanly but leaves the ground with a dragging movement. Okenyi knows he is following an elephant with a limp, and that this may make it bad-tempered and sly. There is nothing in the whole forest as dangerous as a wounded elephant, except perhaps a wounded buffalo. These great beasts get so enraged at their unending torture, a torture which prevents them from sleeping, from following their kind, and which cannot be alleviated by resting because of the terrible pangs of hunger, that they turn evil, and with a mixture of cunning and madness prefer to face their enemy rather than flee, and as often as not kill him.

Okenyi continues to follow his injured quarry through the trees. He finds little dung and notices that the animal's footsteps are rather far apart. Perhaps the elephant had heard the workmen and was moving out of the area. He passes a tree under which lie large numbers of rotting fruits smelling of decay: this is an elephant delicacy, some say the fermenting fruits have an intoxicating effect. This elephant has not stopped: it was in a hurry.

Okenyi tracks his quarry to the edge of the forest and into the tall grassland beyond. He walks between the ten-foot grass walls until his wiry legs are tired and his stomach contracts; he thinks of the distance he must return for food. Resting in a small patch of forest outside the main forest, he debates whether to turn back. A big dark squirrel runs along a branch, and two smaller ones with stripes move around jerkily above, frisking their tails. These squirrels are often found near water: they live over swamps and rarely leave the trees. Looking carefully he sees the glint of water in a shaft of sunlight. He goes over to the pool and drinks. As he drinks he smells the smell of elephant across the water. It is like the majestic theme of a symphony one knows well, a theme from the last movement: all that remains is the finale, and one wonders how well it will be performed.

Okenyi picks up his gun and presses his finger to release the safety catch. He has the smell in his dilated nostrils, his body is half bent, his eyes peering through the trees, his head held forward. He takes a step, pauses, steps again, moving his head this way and that to see between the trees. The smell is strong, it fills the little patch of forest. Every shape is examined with knowledgeable eyes. Especially he looks for the rounded shapes of the elephant, or for a twitch of ears.

With a crash of trees being flung apart the beast moves to his right. He hadn't expected it there. Is it charging or fleeing? He raises his gun. All is quiet. Then he sees it between the trees, at least he sees a shape and knows it is the elephant, though he does not see enough yet. Gently he moves his head and body to get a better view, and finds that by crouching he can see an eye through the leaves. But before he can aim it charges him. At ten yards he aims. It is a young bull in the prime of life; he thinks: impetuous, it should have fled. A chilling shriek pierces the air as the rifle fires. It is a brain shot: death is instantaneous. There is a discordant groan and the elephant staggers, rolling on one side with stiff legs shivering in death. Leaves flutter down, shaken by his fall; insects resume their humming; all around animals resume their lives after the shocked silence when the giant shrieked and fell. Okenyi is tired and content, he looks at his kill and sees the gangrenous left hind foot where a wire snare, since shaken off, had become embedded in the flesh, a buffalo snare probably, never meant for elephant. The beast moves jerkily in death.

The day is humid and overcast as Okenyi returns home. From now until evening he carries his secret with him, for the shot could not be heard in camp six miles away. Tomorrow a hundred men will come to the elephant, to take its meat home for their wives and children. They will come on bicycles and on foot, even some women will undertake the journey. Each will carry home as much as he or she can; Okenyi's fame will ring around the villages. The game guards will take the tusks to be weighed and catalogued and sold, the ears for drying (they sell for twenty shillings, or $2.80, dried, and make excellent shoes and handbags when cured), the feet for paper-baskets, the tail-hairs as lucky charms. Tomorrow will see the elephant opened up and its giant guts displayed, men will wander into its belly cutting off huge slabs of meat. Some will carry it home raw, wrapped in sacking; others smoke it crudely over wood fires, turning it black all over, then pierce the sealed pieces with a pole which they will carry over the shoulder.

And the day after tomorrow nature will send in her squadrons to eat the leftovers. Ants will come, and flies. The flies will breed in thousands and their larvae will feed. Quickly the guts and the meat around the bones and the trunk and the eyes will disappear. Even the skin will be consumed, though it is horny and thick. Rain will wash the blood into the ground. Before a week is over, the huge bones will be displayed, lying in the centre of a small denuded glade, made by the men who first came to take meat and who cut the nearby saplings to make fires and carrying stakes.

Then, months after, we shall come to the spot in our wanderings and see the strewn bones, mouldering now under a fine green mossy cover. We shall stop and look at the wreck and I shall ask Manueri to chip me out a tooth from the jaw, to take home as a souvenir.

One day in April I was up at the mill collecting mail; the day was humid and people were moving about slowly, with a minimum of effort, creeping between the wooden huts as if ashamed of something. Even the giant saws sounded dull and subdued as they ate their way through slice after slice of giant mahogany. I read a letter from England sitting on the office steps, and looked over my latest Kodachrome film to see if there were any good shots of chimpanzees in it. I had just got up to go over to the Land Rover when the heavy peace of the afternoon was interrupted by a party of men returning from the logging point some miles up the track which ran due north. They were in a lorry, and as it passed me they were pointing and shouting something to me, and I thought it contained the word "soko-mutu." I smiled and waved back, embarrassed by this sudden unexpected outburst from twenty or thirty excited men, all directed at me. When the lorry stopped two or three of the men came back to me, and I gathered from their gestures and bits of what they said that a chimpanzee had been caught. It was up the road "milei mbili" (two miles) or something like that. Dropping all other plans, I jumped into the Land Rover and headed up along the north track.

How had they caught it? In a snare? Was it dead, or had they made a cage? My main problem was to find the spot. Some men pointed further up the road, but they probably hadn't understood my question, and I had learnt to distrust people who simply pointed up the road. I took a number of dead-end forks and turned back. Then an empty timber lorry came along heading for the logging point. I drove into the edge of the forest to let him pass, then followed his bouncing trailer truck with its chains and springs banging and crashing along through the dust until suddenly, ahead of us, was a big group of Africans, red bulldozers, freshly felled and trimmed trees awaiting collection, and a wide-open space beyond: the logging area.

The men were sitting in a circle, on logs or on the ground, laughing. In the middle of the circle, tied to a stake, with her arms stretched up above her head and her legs stretched down, lay an old female chimpanzee, a dear old lady, such as many I had seen going about their unobtrusive business in the forest. As I joined the circle of onlookers they continued to joke, while the poor creature alternately shrieked with fear or hooted to her fled companions, turning her head to left and right as she lay on her back, and looking at me piteously as I examined her bonds. She was firmly tied up, by the wrists and ankles, as a wild pig or duiker is tied, so that it can be carried. How far, I wondered, had they brought her, how much had she endured?

I was no missionary; I knew that in Uganda the African's attitude to wild animals in general was catch and kill and eat. The very same word, "nyama," is Swahili for both "animal" (alive) and "meat" (dead or cooked). I had learnt not to expect sympathy and soft feelings for animals in Africa. Yet I had until now believed that the chimpanzee was regarded in a different way from other creatures, that it was a "half-man," whom one respected and left alone and, in particular, never ate. Indeed, generally this was so.

I looked around at the logging men. They were a mixed crowd, from the Congo and Ruanda and all parts of Uganda. In the eastern Congo, I had been told, the people still ate chimpanzees, as they had done in Livingstone's day, ninety years ago.

The men were watching me now, waiting to see my reaction to the situation. Conscious of the imperfections of my Swahili, I started battle. "Where did you catch this chimpanzee?" I asked, to all and sundry. There was no reply, nobody wanted to talk. I think they sensed my fury. I picked on one man. "Over there?" I asked, "or over there?" Suddenly a boy broke ranks with a flood of words, pointing to his leg, and another boy joined him. I gathered that they had been working when the chimp attacked the boy and wanted to kill him; the boy had fought and cried out, whereupon four men had between them pinned the creature down. I looked at his leg—it was scratched slightly—little white scratch marks covered it, such as Manueri got from walking through the rattan. "Where is the blood?" I asked. "If the chimpanzee attacked you, where are the wounds?" A man threw a hard piece of fruit to the chimpanzee, hitting it on the head. I gave up a reasoned approach, and shouted at them all. "Watcha!"—"Leave it! This is bad. It is bad to catch a chimpanzee, bad to tie it up, this is a good animal. This is not food, it is not a duiker. And it is not a lion to be afraid of. I am angry that you have caught it; now we will let it go!"

I summoned two men to take the pole, told the rest to wait behind, and walked into the forest. This was mainly in order that they would not be able to follow her, and also to avoid the risk of her attacking, in case she really was dangerous. She never ceased her howling and screaming. We walked a short distance in, then set her down. I undid her legs—she did not kick wildly as I had expected her to, but fell silent. Gently and without showing fear, I began to unleash her arms. I was expecting at any moment that she would spring up and leap away from us, disappearing forever into the trees. Instead she lay there, placidly watching me as I undid her wrists, a look of what seemed great sadness in her eyes. I ordered the men to stand back and pulled the liana free as gently as I could. Her arms fell out sideways, she moved them a little, she tried to turn on her side, her legs moved a little, she looked at me in despair. She was unable to move away.

During the next half hour I felt her all over to see how she was injured, and discovered an injury to her spine, half way along the back. It was visible under the skin—the vertebrae suddenly changed direction. She could still move her legs a little, but would never walk again.

As she lay on the ground in front of me with pleading eyes, I knew the most merciful thing to do would be to kill her. With a rifle shot, death would be instantaneous, but my gun was sixteen miles away. Or I could cut her throat with a panga. Looking at her, she seemed so intensely human that I could not bear the thought: it would be pure murder. I told the men to stay here and wait for my return; they were to watch the chimpanzee and see if her condition improved; I would be back in one hour with the gun. I slipped them a shilling each and left, satisfied I had made the right choice.

In fact, I had been thoroughly foolish. But that is jumping ahead too far. When I left, passing through the lines of workmen whose fun I had spoiled, I felt their eyes burning through my neck. They probably thought I was stupid and pathetic,

letting a prize like that go free. I hoped they would not notice that the two men who went in with me did not come
out. And, in all probability they would not have noticed; but
then knocking-off time arrived.

So, as I was driving back as fast as I could go for my gun,
bouncing and slithering down the sawmill track, a "rota" was
being called back at the logging area as the day's work ended.
And before I had even reached home a search was on for
the missing men and they were found and so was the chimpanzee. That, at any rate is my theory; I never discovered the
truth. When I returned not a soul was around, there was
nothing on the spot where the old mother chimp had been
except the pole she was strung to and a few broken lianas.
There were no chimpanzee footprints away from the spot,
there was also no blood. Birds sang in the trees, among them
a yellow-bill which cackled at me. A light wind moved the
tree-tops and the first wisps of cloud were forming overhead.
Insects droned in the strong vertical shafts of sunlight: nowhere was there any evidence of the little drama which had
unfolded here. The end must have been sinister and tragic; I
did not think about it. Climbing back into the Land Rover,
with a final curse at my stupidity, I realised I was totally exhausted, and started the bumpy drive home.

CHAPTER EIGHT

Tracking and Finding

It is dawn; let us set off on foot and look for chimpanzees. We shall follow some forest tracks. First, we go down to the main road and turn left. Two hundred yards along on the right a vehicle track goes off through fifty yards of grassland dotted about with cork trees and plunges into the forest. This is a Forest Department road, the one we took on our first day; we have christened it Track A. It is cut twice a year, and in addition fallen trees are cleared as they occur in order to keep the road open at all times. We use this road more than any other; I know every bump and rut along it, when to drive on the left and when on the right, where to park, where to turn, how to cross the plank bridge at the bottom of the first slope. Also we have walked down it innumerable times. There are snares along it, set by Forest Department workmen, and we remove these as we find them. Animal tracks criss-cross it every few yards—old ones mainly, which we already know. A civet has its lavatory in the middle of the road—a big pile of fruit stones and black fecal matter, which grows a little from time to time. To the right a quarter of a mile down is our own track to the fig-tree where we watched chimps every day for a week in April, a little further is the spot where we once lay to watch them crossing the road. An elephant-shrew which lives here—the one Okenyi saw—crosses ahead of us. Down at the bridge we look at the gurgling Bubwe on its way to Lake Albert with some of the forest's surplus rainfall. Here is where I shot the black-lipped cobra. Now we reach Track R.P.5 leading off at right angles to the right, a forest trace marking the boundary between two plots, and heading due south. Ahead is a stretch of a hundred yards on which we often see a male blue duiker browsing along the verge of the road, but he is not here today. At the brow of the hill a party of redtail monkeys jumps around in the trees, squeaking at us and looking incensed, with white noses and rusty-coloured tails darting about in among the greenery. We do not stop, for they would only panic and run off. Distantly a blue monkey makes his alarm call "Kyoh!" and a colobus takes it up with its gargling, oft-repeated belch.

We walk downhill now and there is, as always, a puddle at the bottom. We have never seen any living thing in this dip, although the forest is perfectly ordinary. That is an odd thing, however, and recurrently true—that along any given road or journey, some spots are always full of wild life and others are completely empty. At the top of the slope we curve right and are joined by what we call Track B, cutting in at an angle from our right-hand side. To the left a forest trace, heavily overgrown, goes due north. Ahead of us now is Little Kasenene Hill, which we see from our home, but it cannot be seen from the forest floor and our road goes past it, leaving it unseen on the right-hand side. As we pass the hill a large troop of baboons fills the road ahead, looking at us, scampering about, wiping their snouts, stamping their feet, and barking: "Wo-hrrr, wo-hrr, wo, wo." There are mothers with infants clinging under them, others with infants on their backs, young skinny ones, medium-sized ones, and big bully males with huge ruffs making their heads seem round from the front and their eyes small like pigs'. They are a uniformly olive colour.

As we draw nearer they hop and run, one by one, into the forest.

Past Little Kasenene the road begins a long wind around towards the left (north). We pass the place of the dead trees where we gather firewood, the overgrown track leading off to the right which used to lead to the mill and was used for logging, but is now almost invisible in places and used mainly by buffaloes, whose tracks have made ruts in the grass. Further along on the right is our marker to the tree we discovered one day, a tall beautiful tree with fruits the size of tennis balls and peach-coloured, full of sticky orange flesh from which the white latex poured copiously; Manueri bit into the fruits greedily after examining them, and said they were "Mzuri sana, sasa pombe!"—"Very good, like beer!," and vowed to return and collect more as they fell. We later discovered this species to be *Mammea africana,* a very rare tree found, in Uganda, only in the Budongo Forest. Past this marker the road dips, rises, and turns to the point where it doubles back on itself, from north-west to north-east; at this point a forest trace we call R.P.2 heads off in a line towards the west, continuing past the Forest Department store, where diesel and spraying equipment used in the poisoning of trees are kept in a round tin hut, right up to the edge of the forest. Following Track A (but we shall go no further) we could fork left further ahead along a road which leads out of the forest amid a flourish of flame trees, into the elephant grass and to the Sonso River beyond, wide here and uncrossable; or we could take the right fork which stays inside the forest and meanders gently downwards, with elephant trails to left and right, to the sad wreck of the Sonso River bridge, brought down some months ago by a swollen river and now, with its structure weakened and some of its planks missing, in urgent need of repair. The broken bridge is in a delightful glade, the river gurgles here on its way through, and for some reason grass grows beneath the ironwood trees. Crossing the bridge by foot is still possible, but the glade is so enchanting, and the road ahead so overgrown, that we have never gone much further than this point.

No chimpanzees call; the morning is lost. Feeling hungry, we settle down with our backs to trees and Frankie pulls the sandwiches out of our leather bag. One sandwich each, Budongo beef as ever. Manueri politely takes his with an "Asante sana, Mama"—"Thank you very much, Mother." We all begin chewing, the meat defends itself remorselessly. Little crumbs of bread fall onto the leaves and we watch as, almost immediately, ants collect them and take them off, two or three working together on the larger ones, to their home in some nearby crevice or perhaps up in a tree.

Manueri makes one of his cigarettes and lights up. The dense grey smoke turns blue as it coils upwards in shafts of sunlight between the trees. We lean back, resting. Suddenly Manueri says, "Ndege"—a bird. Distantly, we detect the faintest droning far up in the sky; coming a little closer, it is definitely an aeroplane, the first we have heard for months. We listen carefully as it comes a very little closer and then passes out of earshot, bound on its distant purpose. We find a smile on our lips, Frankie and I, for it reminds us of a whole world whose existence we had forgotten, a frantic civilisation hurrying, hurrying.

"Sisi nakuja hapa kwa ndege sasa hi," I venture to Manueri —"We came out here on a plane like that one."

"Oh!" His whole expression invites me to go on.

"A plane is not small, it is big, and heavy!"

"Oh! As big as an elephant!"

"Bigger!"

"Oh! Completely big!"

"Yes. And fifty people can go in it!"

"Fifty?" He is incredulous. "No." He rejects the idea.

"Yes, fifty and more! And we came here above the clouds!"

"Phew." His long-drawn whistle of astonishment. "The plane goes above the clouds? It must be very hot."

"No, it is very cold outside the plane, but good inside. If you look out of the plane you can see the forests and the plains and the mountains—everything!"

"Good." He imagines himself up there, looking down, then fear strikes him. "Mimi hapana penda ndege"—"I don't like planes."

"Why not?"

"That's very far up. Bad. If there is a breakdown, boom!" Gesturing with a downwards sweep of his hand.

"Yes," we agree, "that is bad. But if you travel many days on foot you may eat bad food and die; in the plane the food is very good and the journey is very quick. How long do you think it takes to go to Ingereza [England]?"

"Wiki tatu," he guesses—"Three weeks."

"No. From Entebbe to London it takes eleven hours."

"Ow! The plane goes 'pessi-pessi!' [very quickly!] Eleven hours, and England is beyond West Nile!"

"Beyond West Nile," we point out, "is the Sudan. The Sudan is bigger than all of Uganda. Beyond the Sudan is Egypt. Egypt is bigger than all of Uganda. Beyond Egypt is a big sea with much water, which is bigger than Uganda. Beyond that sea is Europe; Europe is bigger than all of Uganda. At the other side of Europe is England."

We are all speechless for a while at the thought of it.

"It needs many shillings to go to London," he says.

"Yes. Many shillings. How many do you think?"

"People say it needs two thousand shillings."

"Yes. That is right." We are surprised he knows. He shakes his head and says "A-a." We get up and start walking, slowly, for the mention of that vast sum has made the conversation sad. Not that he is envious; he has never even had the desire to go to Kampala. But the social inequality between us has been exposed and we are aware of it, each with an equal regret.

We now return down Track A to the junction with Track B and follow that road. It leads off through grassland, circuiting the hill, and here red-legged partridges, or francolins, feed on the path, on the alert because of the barks of baboons watching us from arboreal posts up the hillside. After half a mile we enter the forest through its surrounding jacket of *Maesopsis* trees; it quickly ages and becomes higher, more diverse, and more grown about with lianas and the other trappings of maturity until we are on a gentle slope down to the Lwenti River. This slope is favoured by guinea-fowl and I have often shot them here, also I have twice watched a ram bush-buck which frequents these parts, and admired the beauty of his spots and stripes and his foot-long horns. The river itself is bridged over for vehicles to pass, but the surrounding land and indeed the whole valley is marshy, marked on the map of forest types as swamp-forest. This is the result of the shape of the valley which, perhaps because it is a new watercourse, is not a deep cut into the soil but a mere declivity on either side, and the river meanders down the middle in a hundred little rivulets interspersed with marshland and the trees and creepers that grow on it: rattan, *Pseudospondias*, the liana that, if you cut a piece of it off, pours forth water which you can drink, and others. So, when crossing the Lwenti bridge by vehicle, I have learnt to take it at a good speed or risk getting stuck in the mud on the gently rising far slope. But today on foot this is a pleasant bridge to linger by, and look along the marshy valley with its unusual trees and squirrels and insects and, above all, frogs. Round the next bend, we reach the spot where a particular tree used to stand. One day, as we were walking through the forest, we heard a tree fall and Manueri said it was this very tree and it was. He had seen its gigantic frailty weeks before. When it fell, after a rainstorm, it came down like a house of cards, straight downwards not sideways, in little pieces, rotten through and through.

Further along is the place where we ourselves were struck by a falling tree as we drove down the road. We were bumping along when all of a sudden, for no reason that I could see, I lost all control and the Land Rover went straight round into the forest on the left-hand side of the track. I thought the steering must have gone. We got out a bit bruised but uninjured and, looking backwards, saw that the whole of the road behind us was blocked by the topmost branches of a big tree which must, at the instant of our passing, have been falling towards the road from its position a hundred feet inside the forest. A branch had caught the Land Rover slap across the roof, tearing the canvas to shreds and wrenching the metal roof frame off, but there was no other damage. Had the tree fallen a fraction of a second sooner, the branch would have landed on our heads. We looked at the fallen tree—it was one which had been poisoned by the Forest Department, until then our biggest benefactors in Uganda. With a few muttered curses we backed out onto the track and continued on up to the mill for roof repairs.

Track B was quite a track for falling wood. A little further along from the place where we were struck we found, one day, a huge limb of an otherwise healthy mahogany tree lying across the road. The branch itself was almost as thick as a man's height, for I afterwards used it as a blind when out after kanga, and shot one at one hundred yards with the gun resting on it. Why had it dropped? Perhaps a tornado had struck it, and I mean that seriously for we had a tornado one night at the bottom of our hill and it brought down a row of trees like a giant scythe. Past this great leafy chunk of fallen mahogany which left a great red-brown wound a hundred feet up on the side of its parent, the track runs straight for several hundred yards and there are usually monkeys, redtails or colobus, along this stretch. At the bottom is a giant mukunyu fig-tree on the right but it is not in season now. Then the track turns right and right again and we are out on the road to the sawmill, standing on gravel, with every now and then a man on foot or on a bicycle going by.

Still no chimp calls. It is a bad day. Tired as we are, we must try somewhere else. We go down to the dusty, red main road, turn right, and walk along it a full mile towards Busingiro until we reach a spot where, on the right, is a white milestone saying "27" on the near side and "17" on the far side—twenty-seven miles to Masindi, seventeen to Butiaba the other way. Behind this stone the bank of the road rises— three feet or so of exposed red soil; it is covered in grass on top, and three feet or so behind this bank is the edge of the forest. Looking carefully, a hole can be seen at this point. Taking care not to slip, as the bank slopes steeply downwards through the hole, we enter the forest. Ahead of us is a forest trace running due east; it marks the boundary between two Forest Department plots and is cleared once a year. We call it the Mile 27 East Track. We walk along it between *Maesopsis* trees at first, on a gentle downhill slope, conscious of the coolness of the air under the trees.

A short way along is a fallen tree-trunk which can be crossed as follows: you step on the branch, which is firm and springy and about a foot off the ground; from this you step up onto the main trunk—careful, it is slippery and inclined to crumble—walk along it obliquely to the track for four paces, and then jump off. Ahead we approach the First Valley. This is very steep and we leave the Mile 27 East Track, going very slightly off to the left where our stakes are waiting for us. We take one each and begin the descent, picking our steps on the firmer parts of the ground and using the stick either to lean on or sticking it into the ground just ahead and stepping on the ground behind it so that the stick itself is holding the foot from slipping. We get to the bottom, where the Bubwe River trickles along between large and small stones, with shrubs growing in the mud and the footpads of a leopard between the shrubs, hoofprints of a red duiker too, and a yel-

low caterpillar with long black hair and red eyes sitting on a
leaf. We cross the river over stepping stones. On the far side
the fruits of a "mujgangoma" tree litter the forest floor, looking like huge acorns complete with cups, but they are sticky
inside and have a stone; we turn left and follow the bank of
the stream a few yards, crawl under a fallen tree which is
worn smooth with the rubbing of our backs, and rejoin the
Mile 27 East Track for the ascent. Now we use our sticks
to push on as we clamber slowly up the slippery slope, finding
step-like footholds wherever we can. To our right is a fig-tree
visited by the chimpanzees when it is in fruit, but at present
it isn't. A little pale-blue flower, like a pansy, shows through
the shrubs. At the top we stick our sticks into their accustomed place near a rotten tree-stump, ready for the return.

The ground now slopes gently upwards. A group of colobus
monkeys flash black and white, crashing from branch to
branch with great leaps in the tree-tops ahead. We pass three
ironwood trees which throw their buttresses across our path
like a barrier, and find a porcupine's quill under one of them.
At the top of the gentle slope is a big flat stone. We start
downwards on the undulation. So far Manueri today has not
used the knife, an index of our ill-luck; we have not exerted
ourselves, walking along at a steady pace, silently, in tune
with the forest. For a fallen tree we leave the path, turning
off after a smooth-barked tree, to the left, going in a wide
semicircle marked by chips on the trees, stepping over a fallen
branch two feet up and rejoining the Mile 27 East Track at
the slope towards the Second Valley. Again the steep descent
but here, for some reason, we do not use sticks. To our left a
giant mahogany lies across the entire valley, an enormous
bridge, but we do not use it, for a slip would mean a drop of
thirty feet. This is a dry valley—even after a rain a proper
stream does not run along it—yet it must in the past have
been a big carving stream like the Bubwe.

A recently fallen tree lies along the line of our path on the far side of the valley: we use its small resilient branches to pull ourselves up, but it is a nuisance and we ought to make a detour at this point. Manueri stops and points: a bush-buck stands ahead of us on the track; he turns and leaps into the forest with a shattering bark, then two or three more, each more muffled than the last as he runs into the trees: "Wo!!! Wo!! Wo!" Birds do not cease their calling at this alarm, soft piping notes and cackles and the distant caw-caw-ing of hornbills go on unabated; the flashing scarlet of a but-terfly catches our eye; we go on up the slope. Here a liana hangs in a vertical line, dropping 150 feet from a branch and still not reaching the ground, its red, naked roots suspended in the air searching for soil, growing slowly downwards. There is no wind above, the leaves are still.

Chimpanzee calls ahead! There are some in the Third Val-ley. We go on at a slightly quickened pace. The path widens out a little here and begins to slope very gently downwards; Manueri uses the knife sometimes to slice through the *Ma-rantochloa* shrubs with their juicy stems and broad leaves—they fall sideways like toppled pins, leaving us a clear path. The Third Valley is not steep, indeed there is no true valley, just a gentle slope to the bottom. Leaving the track to our left, we go more slowly now, picking our way between the trees, pausing every now and then to scan the tree-tops ahead. We reach the spot where there are some "muyati" trees (*Mild-braediodendron*) which we know to be fruiting, and stop to listen. We sit down to wait; we are too close to risk moving now. All is still, then a quarrel breaks out ahead, excited screaming and some gruff barks. We know just where they are, and we edge forward, step by step.

First we see an adult male sitting on a branch, chewing a strip of bark. He moves out of the way as another male comes along—did the latter snatch his bark? There are screams and a brief chase in the trees behind. An adolescent male with a pale face appears on a branch of the muyati—he thumps the branch with his feet, holding on with his arms. The adult male scratches himself, then begins feeding on the big green muyati fruits, peeling them first with his teeth, then chewing up the fleshy inside (which looks like cucumber), and finally spitting out the rest of the peel in a chewed-up mass. He moves off looking for food, out of sight. We wait. Manueri settles down and lights a cigarette.

After a few minutes a mother walks into sight, her toto clinging beneath her belly. She sits down and feeds; the baby drops to the branch and gingerly walks along it, to a big elephant's-ear fern which it slaps with one hand. It has a pink face and a white "tail-tuft." All is quiet but for the buzzing of insects and bird-calls, and the occasional rustle of leaves as a chimpanzee strips off a branch for food, and the thud-thud of overripe fruits as they fall to the ground.

We watch and make notes for an hour; we see five chimps; sometimes they call but never very loudly. One by one they drift away, out of sight, and then deep into the forest; we follow a little but without conviction—it is growing late and we shall not see them again—and so we consult and decide to turn for home.

Working outwards from our base at Busingiro Hill, we had found that the most useful thing we could do was to concentrate all our efforts on an area of about sixteen square miles, within which we could, most days, hear a group somewhere or other. This we called our area of study and, although we frequently went beyond it to follow up particular groups or for other reasons, the bulk of our work was done within this chunk of trees. Every forest type was represented here, although there was not much ironwood forest, but this type, we had established, was not very favourable chimpanzee habitat anyway. Our chunk was mainly mixed, woodland, and *Maesopsis* forest, with its fair share of swamps, and we had both the solid mass of forest on the Budongo side and the narrow strips of riverine forest in the Siba to work in. We found no area of natural forest which the chimpanzees shunned entirely, but we quickly established that certain areas were favourite chimp localities, and as time went by we saw how these favoured places changed every so often with the fruits and seasons.

We had gathered a lot of information in our first months about their feeding habits, daily routines, and social life, but our project title included a second heading, and one which began to interest us more and puzzle us more as time went by. That heading was "social *organisation*." The idea that chimpanzees live in "family groups" is widespread today, both in white societies and in Africa itself. Where this idea comes from it is impossible to say—is it perhaps that we humans tend to be anthropomorphic whenever we think of apes, and attribute our own kind of social life to them? Several authors have committed themselves to print on the point: David Livingstone, for instance, wrote of chimpanzees in his *Last Journals*: "They live in communities of about ten, each having his own female. . . . If one tries to seize the female of another, he is caught on the ground, and all unite in boxing and biting the offender." Is this not a case of Victorian family morality imposed on the chimp?

At all events, to judge from the writings of a good many naturalists who saw chimpanzees in the wild, no such family groups exist. Robert Garner, for example, stated, "I have never been able to see a family of them together," and he reported that of several groups of chimpanzees which he had watched crossing an open space from one patch of forest to another, the groups numbered from two to ten individuals, and none consisted of a "family." Henry Nissen's study of chimpanzees in West Africa produced no evidence of permanent groupings, family or otherwise.

Shortly before we set out for Uganda, Adriaan Kortlandt, a Dutch zoologist, had made a study of wild chimpanzees on a plantation site near Beni, in the East Congo, and had obtained no evidence of family groups. He had gone further, and said that there were no *permanent* groups of chimpanzees at all—that the animals come and go as they please; when they do join up, they form either "nursery groups," consisting of a gathering of mothers and their infants, or "sexual groups," consisting of adult males and females.

Besides this question of groups, there were two other problems which, we realised, were as yet totally uninvestigated, and naturally we determined to concentrate on them. One was the question of whether a particular number of chimpanzees could be thought of as a "tribe," as opposed to other "tribes" in the forest. And the second arose directly out of this—were there particular areas of forest which were more or less exclusively ranged over by particular sets of chimpanzees? Or were we faced with a large number of chimps, none of which knew or cared much about each other, which roamed the forest from one fruit area to another without any allegiance to, or special knowledge of, any particular tract of trees?

We guessed that we would need a vast body of information to be able to answer these complex questions. In the meantime we concentrated on the simpler issues. For a start, we compared the society of chimpanzees with that of baboons. Baboons live in "troops," a troop being a number of primates which live together permanently. With chimpanzees, we came to realise, everything was different. In the fig season when we first began our observations, groups had been large and noisy, fifteen or more chimps on a tree. Then in the lean season, groups had been small and scattered and sometimes single individuals were encountered feeding alone. Then, in the igeria season, once again we met with large noisy mixed feeding groups. There was never any indication that a group of chimpanzees was a constant unit.

For three weeks in June we had the opportunity to observe and examine the membership of chimpanzee groups at close quarters in good observation conditions. Over the study area the chief fruit in season was the damson-like igeria, and we were finding it difficult observing in the swamps, because of recent heavy rainfall, and also because, at this season, chimps never seemed to stay long on one patch of igeria trees, but were forever moving on after half an hour or so. We had to find somewhere better to continue our observations for the time being. Down the road towards Masindi was a large coffee estate called Kanyege, and a neighbour, Don Bagley, now told us that chimpanzees were calling there. Imagine our delight when, one dismal misty dawn, we negotiated our Land Rover, slithering and skidding along the wet muddy soil between the coffee bushes to the far side of the estate where it bordered the forest, and Manueri spotted movements in the trees fringing the estate. "Soko-mutu!" he said. We stopped the vehicle and got out. Then, dodging from coffee bush to coffee bush, each time getting a cold shower of fresh rain down our necks, we approached the outline of trees. Arrived at the end of the bushes, and in direct view of the moving branches, we each selected a coffee bush as camouflage and sat down behind it to observe. We half expected disappointment—that the movements would turn out to be monkeys of some sort. But no, they were chimps, and they were feeding on nyakatomas. We were in luck. They had not seen us. Every morning for the next three weeks chimps came to these trees, and we were there first thing every day, squatting damply behind our chosen coffee bushes, identifying, counting, and observing.

After a few hours, by mid-morning, the chimps in the trees at the edge of the estate left to visit other feeding areas, and at this point we would follow one group, though we found this particular stretch of the Siba Forest very difficult to locate chimps in. It was a wavy finger of gallery forest fringing the Siba River, and the chimps always seemed to be calling on the bank opposite to us. The only way to cross the swollen river, which was fifteen to twenty feet wide, six feet deep, and swirling and muddy, was to walk across by a fallen tree-trunk straddling the stream. Manueri cut strong staffs from saplings for each of us and gingerly we edged our way across, testing each foot-hold on the crumbling rotten logs. But usually we expended enormous efforts only to see the last chimpanzee leaving the trees, for these were a restless lot of chimps. One day they led us deep into the forest and out onto the grass-land beyond, where we found the fresh green dung, still warm, of a herd of elephants which had been there only minutes previously. The Siba was "kali" (wild) forest, as Manueri so often said.

But whereas inside the forest we gained little extra infor-mation, those hours from dawn at the Kanyege coffee estate yielded much raw material. Some chimps were there day after day, and always in a favourite spot in the clump of trees. There were two huge black-faced matrons, each with a three-year-old juvenile. The two juveniles played together while the mothers sat there solemnly reaching for fruit, plucking, chewing, spitting, and reaching again. Unlike human mothers, they never chattered to each other. These two were always the first to arrive in the morning, and the last to leave. They probably did not go far away, and slept in the trees close be-hind. Another regular visitor, who arrived on his own and had his own spot in a tree to the left of the mothers, was "Pink-ears" an adult male whose sparse hair allowed his pink skin to show through in a number of places, and who sported an enormous pair of floppy ears. A fourth early arrival was usu-ally "Cheeky Charlie," an adolescent who would come right out onto the edges of the branches overlooking the estate. Though he often spotted us behind our inadequate coffee-bush hides, he never ran away, but peered and stared at us and moved to get a better view. Of these four only the two mothers arrived together, the two males came singly at different times, but all seemed to come from a sleeping place fairly close by.

As the sun began to clear the mist from the tree-tops, excited calls came from a finger of forest which lay away to the east along the river, and as the calls got louder and closer, three large mature adult males bounded along hitting trees, stamping, and hollering as they approached the spot where the four were feeding. As they arrived and clambered up, there was always some commotion in the trees which died down after a minute or two, as the adult males settled down to feeding in their favourite places. These males never remained for more than half an hour. Other choruses came from about a mile to the west, from the large part of the Siba Forest proper, and these our males answered, eventually making off towards them. The mothers, on the other hand, with Pink-ears, when they had finished their early morning feed, used to retreat towards the river where other chimps, among them some other females, were feeding on a swampy igeria patch. These were regular visitors, but each day of the first week and from time to time after that there were other individuals not seen before and not recognised again. Thus if these chimps all belonged to one group, then it was not a socially compact unit —it did not sleep in one area, did not come or go in the same direction, did not have the same daily routines, and was not always composed of the same individuals.

The only way to find out if certain chimps always associated together was by recognising individuals. This was a simple thing to do when we had the good luck to find a fruiting tree with a group including it in its round of visits for a number of days, as was described above. A good vantage point could be chosen while the chimps were away, and positions taken up before their arrival; the visitors each day were then described and compared with those of all the previous days. But the majority of our days were jungle-bashing days in which we tracked calls and caught glimpses of bits of chimps high up in the trees, and could never be certain of the identity of any individual. We had, however, seen enough to know that if chimps had permanent groups they were loosely organised ones, in which small bands of twos, threes, fours, or fives travelled through the forest, meeting and joining others, splitting up and going various ways. We knew that large and noisy groups assembled when the sources of food were concentrated, as in the fig season, and that when fruit was scarce or widely scattered, the chimps made little noise, and were found foraging singly or dispersed in twos and threes. We had obtained no evidence of "families"—there had never been any sign of particular males associating with particular mothers; on the contrary, mothers tended to keep together. Perhaps they did this for the sake of each other's company, or perhaps they sought extra safety in numbers. At all events, we found that these groups of mothers with their young were extremely difficult to find and observe in our forest conditions. For mothers were cautious and suspicious. If one of them noticed a chance movement or a flashing lens, without waiting to ascertain what the cause of the unusual stimulus was, off they all clambered with offspring clasped to their bellies, and silently they were lost along the maze of chimp tracks. Another difficulty was finding them in the first place, for they were in general far less vociferous than the other adults, often staying in one patch of trees for hours or even days at a time, and not advertising their presence, except by very occasional little barks or squeals. Thus it was far more difficult for us to take a bearing and track off towards them. However, sometimes we struck lucky, and when we did get a few hours' good observations of a party of mothers and babies it was well worth the trouble.

For example, over Easter we had some really good fortune. We had been having a bad time, as groups seemed very small and were always moving about, food being scarce. One day near the end of April we had more or less given up for the day, having heard few calls, and having had no success tracking those. Manueri had run out of "posho," and it was time we drove to the mill as the Land Rover was in need of petrol and oil. So we set off on the seven-mile drive along the bumpy track. We were just negotiating the slippery muddy wooden bridge over the Kamirambwa River when Manueri shouted "Soko-mutu!" so suddenly that I braked and nearly ditched us into the water. We followed his pointing finger and there, incredibly, just by the roadside, in a huge sprawling fig-tree, were at least a score of chimps feeding nonchalantly in full view! We thought they might leave when they saw us watching, and one or two did, but most remained, giving us no more than an occasional glance. The best explanation for this is that the chimps knew the road was human territory and that therefore humans on it did not present a "threat." In the forest, it is different; there humans are on animal territory and are therefore suspect. This theory was proved when, on one occasion, we tried moving closer to some "tame" roadside chimps by entering the forest a little way towards them, whereupon they hurriedly left.

So we sat down casually on the gravel, and started taking notes. There were four mothers in the tree. Two had quite small infants, of two years old or less, and one of these was that rare but not unknown freak a ginger-haired baby, ginger-coloured all over except for its face, which was sandy brown. Another mother had a small infant and a larger one of three or four years. The fourth had what we estimated to be a three-year-old. In addition there was a young adolescent female that might have been the elder offspring of one of the mothers. Also in the tree were two other adult females and an old grandma with a bald rump, grey hair, and a rheumaticky walk. A big powerful male was there at first, and we thought perhaps he was looking after the females, but he soon swung off with a hoot in answer to calls from further away, and we saw no more of him.

A delightful panorama of childish play now ensued. One of the infants was playing with the three-year-old juvenile. The juvenile stood up on all fours and the infant scrambled on its back. Then the infant swung underneath to hang below the juvenile's belly. They were obviously playing at "mothers and babies." The juvenile put an arm round the infant but the infant scrambled free and started jumping up and down on top of the juvenile, which now lay down. As the infant swung above the juvenile, the juvenile reached up and plonked a kiss on its tiny bottom! Frankie kept saying "Ah!"; it really was very human and amusing. Later the other toto and the juvenile and the adolescent all joined in and played a chasing game, swinging, falling, running; for half an hour they kept this up. At one point one of the juveniles was being chased up a branch by a toto, and the juvenile kept stamping on the reaching hands of the infant below! When the mothers decided to leave later in the afternoon, the youngsters were still playing, and as they left, the adolescent female popped one of the infants beneath her and carried it off in place of the mother.

Very young infants, of six months or less, remain nestled close to the mother or swing just above her. When she moves, the tiny baby clings below her belly, and if it is very small it is difficult to spot. At about a year it is becoming more adventurous, and plays and does acrobatics on the branches close by its mother. Later still, in the next few years it will ride on her back, piggy-back style, though if frightened, or when she travels fast, it will revert to the belly position. Mothers are usually tolerant of the antics of small infants, as they explore the environment and test their own capabilities. We once watched a baby dancing up and down on its mother's head, clinging to a small overhanging branch, and another time saw one swinging round and round her neck while she attempted to feed! Chimpanzee mothers tend, rather like human ones, to herd together, presumably on the basis of common interest, in groups of two to five mothers. The offspring then form active play-groups.

One day in early July we were able to test a theory we were developing. We had been watching large groups of chimps feeding in some swampy patches of forest in the Siba, rather south of the main forest, where some igerias were ripe. Then one day, we set off as usual to the swamps only to find that, in bands of two or three, our chimps were leaving the swamps and crossing the road eastwards towards the big block of Budongo. All morning this was going on. As a party crossed, it gave loud calls, sometimes answered by those still to cross or those ahead. They did not all cross in one place but in several different ones along a stretch of road about a mile long. Manueri, Frankie, and I spaced ourselves out, and recorded and counted each group we saw. Later Africans and sawmill employees came to us and told us that still other parties were crossing at points of the road we could not cover. Leaving Frankie on the roadside to watch for developments, Manueri and I went in after one large group and tracked it north-eastwards until late afternoon. Calls came from all directions, those ahead, those behind, those on either side, but somehow all the chimps were bearing in the same direction. It seemed that rather than following a particular route, chimps followed the direction of the calls and drums of those who went first. We lost track of the leaders, however; they seemed to be travelling fast deep into Budongo. Back on the road we totalled those we had seen or knew to have crossed during the morning. We counted between twenty and thirty, and among all of these, we knew of only one definite mother and infant. Yet when we had been watching these selfsame chimp groups in the swamps, there had been many mothers and babies. Had they been left behind? Why had they not left with the others now that fruit was becoming scarce in the swamps?

Next morning at dawn we returned to the swamps and listened for calls as the sun slowly appeared. We heard a very few calls and crept cautiously into the forest. They were not far away, coming from one of our well-known igeria patches. Nevertheless, it always takes longer than one could believe possible to get through forest cautiously and quietly, and it was 9:20 A.M. before we saw and heard the branches rustling ahead. We sat down, unwilling to go further, for if, as we suspected, these calls might be coming from the mothers and babies left behind by the males and other females, then we had to be ultra-careful. Manueri leant back against a shadowy tree-trunk and became invisible, his dirty old jacket and black skin merging with the forest. But his eyes searched upwards, his head moving slightly to see beyond and through the leaves and branches. Frankie and I made sure there were covering canopies of leafy branches between us and the tree ahead where we could see the branches moving, and gently raised our binoculars to our eyes, elbows on raised knees, ready for a long wait. A slight chuckle from Manueri's direction made me turn towards him reproachfully. He pointed with his eyes, a big grin on his face. I focussed in the direction he indicated and suddenly a tiny unsuspecting toto came into my field of view. He had been left to amuse himself, so he was running through his repertoire of acrobatics. He was hanging from both arms from a slender branch and bicycling gaily with his legs. Then up he swung his feet, gripped the branch, and let go with his hands, looking round and round, surveying the world from this new angle. Momentarily tiring, he disappeared upwards, but in a minute reappeared and encored the same performance. We timed seven minutes of his solo acrobatics while we watched. Panning the binoculars upwards to where the toto had gone, I could just make out a large black stationary form, no doubt the mother, feeding and glancing towards the toto. Suddenly he gave soft "ee, ee" sounds and looked upwards to the right of his mother. Into view leapt another toto, just slightly older, perhaps three years, and running towards number one, he grasped him, and the two of them rolled about hugging each other, front to front for some minutes. I don't know how they managed not to fall off the branches!

They left our view and for a while we could see nothing, only vague branch movements; then we caught sight of them again. This time they were having a wrestling match, heads low, pummelling each other. This was great fun. Manueri thought it all a tremendous joke and murmured, "Sasa watu" —"Just like people." But there were more fun and games to come. After losing them again among the leaves, we redis- covered our totos, with a *third* one now, sliding down a long swinging liana—the sort used by Tarzan to leap through the jungle—and then, funniest of all, racing back up through the branches simply to slide down again! Once there were two closely following upon each other, and the top one kicked out at the one underneath. They moved out of view and we, with aching eyes, decided to eat our sandwiches. During lunch the adults moved closer to us in the igeria trees, and one, a wary, pregnant old female, must have spotted something, and we just managed to grab our binoculars in time to see them all leaving. In the tree had been three females and one pregnant female, three totos and a young adolescent chimp. When they left it was in the direction of a few soft calls heard earlier in the morning, perhaps some other mothers and babies.

It now seemed that our theory was being proved right. This was that the bands of adult males, often accompanied by childless females and the older adolescent chimps, formed the most active and mobile groups that we saw. Mothers, and other interested females, on the other hand, tended to band together, and remained longer on familiar trees, making less noise. Working on these ideas, and alive to any clues which might help us to see *how* this type of social organisation might have helped the chimpanzees survive in their evolution, we tried to fit in some of the other facts. Firstly, there was the prodigiously loud noise that chimps made when feeding in a tree with masses of fruit, in contrast with their silence when food was scarce; and secondly there was the fact that the bands of active and mobile adult males hooted noisily and, especially, drummed as they moved through the forest. What if the males, powerful and untrammelled by youngsters, were the *food-finders*, announcing their progress through the forest by hooting and drumming, and their success when they found a good tree by creating a tremendous hullaballoo; whereupon first the other adults and then the groups of mothers moved to the new area, having wasted no effort hunting about the forest, but relying on the males for guidance? It was a good theory and we worked on it; as time went by new facts emerged and confirmed it, and to this day we believe that this is the solution which chimpanzees have developed to tackle the problems of forest life.

CHAPTER NINE

Gorillas

Another kind of ape lives in Uganda—the gorilla. Why not try and see some while we were so close by? The more we thought about it, the better the idea seemed to be. Finally we fixed a date, in July, when we would down tools, give Semei and Manueri a couple of weeks off, and head south to gorilla-land. And in due course that date arrived.

We weren't just "going to see the gorillas." What we hoped for was a *contrast*, chimp versus gorilla, which might help us to see the chimpanzee's particular adaptations more clearly, for the gorilla, superficially just a larger version of the chimpanzee, is in fact very different in many ways. We knew something of these differences from reading and from hearing about George Schaller's excellent study of these mountain gorillas, then just completed. Apart from the question of size —gorilla males are fully three times as big as chimpanzee males, and females are twice as big—there was the matter of social organisation. Unlike the Budongo chimpanzees, we knew from Schaller's studies that gorillas live in fairly small, permanent groups, the members of each group keeping in contact with each other at all times, and we knew that each group was led by a single big silver-backed male. *Why* this outstanding difference from the chimpanzees, with their loose, dispersed society and lack of permanent groups and leaders?

Schaller had shown the gorilla to be mainly a terrestrial creature—big males in particular very rarely climb trees. And together with this goes the ground diet of gorillas—pithy stems, leaves, roots, and bark being their main source of nourishment, while fruits provide no more than a supplement. How different from the chimpanzees, happiest when they can gorge themselves on fruits for hours at a time, high in the tree-tops. This difference of food habits was, we felt, of fundamental importance and might help to explain other problems such as the difference in social organisation.

There were other intriguing questions; why does the gorilla soil its nest with dung every night, while the chimpanzee keeps its nest scrupulously clean, performing its natural functions over the edge? And why is the chimpanzee one of the noisiest, most vocal creatures in creation, while gorillas are quiet most of the time? And finally the most teasing question of all—why should gorillas have a morose, sullen, placid temperament, while chimpanzees are volatile, lively, and excitable? The more we thought about it, the more we realised how different the two species were.

Turning these questions over in our minds, we drove along the damp red gravel road towards Fort Portal, the first town on our southward route. It was now the wet season in this part of the country, no bush-fires, no dust trail. If only we could see those gorillas! We had met people who had gone on this very quest without success, who had returned tired and disappointed but vowing to try again, such is the magnetic attraction of these giant apes.

From Fort Portal, we took the road down into Ankole District, a bare country of hills and plains, with here and there a huge herd of cattle, lean but with giant curved horns: the famous Ankole cattle, more beautiful than any others in the world. How they managed to support the huge weight of those horns we often wondered; it was a thought which, quite obviously, had never entered their lovely heads. Here the cattle are not as sacred as they are in India, but neither do they exist simply for food—in addition, they are regarded as a source of wealth and are used in bride-wealth transactions. As a result they are left to reproduce among themselves and only barren cows are fattened for killing and eating. We saw the slim herd-boys as we drove through the treeless plain, holding painted gourds from which they drank milk to slake their thirst.

We camped in Ankole, where the land was rising a little towards the mountains further west. That evening three herdsmen came and sat with us, each carrying a long stick; we could not talk to them. At night it grew bitterly cold and we shivered in our sleeping bags; we were already breakfasting as the sun broke through the mist around the hills next day, and were soon on our way through the tinkle of African cow bells towards Kigezi District. And what a contrast it was: rolling mountainous country, cultivated in terraces all the way up and down its steep slopes, no cattle here but dark fertile soil, a happy atmosphere above the subsistence level, beehives long and slim hanging from the trees, flowers, and the road always climbing up ahead, far up into a further range of hills. The people by the roadside were cheerful and had patterned mats for sale; they wore dust-coloured sheets tied around their necks or under one arm, in contrast with the more ragged appearance of the people on our home-ground up in Bunyoro, or in Ankole we had just passed through. There too, in Ankole, the men all carried hunting spears; here they carried lovely baskets full of vegetables on their heads. We bought a basket for a shilling (fourteen cents); it was a work of art.

After a long winding mountainous road we arrived in Kabale, a sleepy town in the midday heat with identical Indian shops in a long row down either side of the street. From Kabale on to little Kisoro township, six thousand feet up, on the Ruanda border. Here we were welcomed by Walter Baumgartel, who runs the world-famous gorilla safari-lodge Travellers Rest. Situated just inside the no-man's-land between Uganda and Ruanda, it is a delightful cluster of gaily decorated and comfortable lodges, and the host himself is the most hospitable and friendliest man alive. Above Travellers Rest loom the volcanoes where the gorillas live, Mt. Muhavura, 13,547 feet, the nearest, Mt. Mgahinga next, and in the distance Mt. Sabinio. As we sat on our verandah in the evening, it seemed unreal that somewhere on those conical slopes, now dimming behind a purple evening mist, some great apes were snatching a final feed and making their nests before retiring for the night, and it seemed even more unreal that next day we should be going up there ourselves. The volcanoes seemed more like a picture on the wall. But later at supper we met a man who had been up that very day and glimpsed them; it was the first time in several weeks, a good omen.

During the evening we were entertained with exquisite African music by Sawa-sawa, an old Batwa beggar who for a shilling sings and plays on a stringed instrument at Travellers Rest. His pygmoid tribe is a servant tribe (or was until the recent revolution), under the tall, superior Watutsi, and the ballads he plays are in an ancient Ruanda tongue known only to these servant bards. His eyes looked wistful as he played, he seemed to sing of love; and then the note changed and he danced about on his old legs, thrusting, thrusting with an imaginary spear, shouting and guffawing and crouching back in fear; was it the hunt or war? Soon he was quiet again and strumming a new and infinitely subtle rhythm.

Most of the people here in Kisoro are neither Batwa nor Watutsi, but a middle group, middle in stature and status: the Wahutu, gay people, whose women wear dozens of gold-coloured bangles round their arms and legs, and are among the most beautiful in all Africa.

Trade had had its ups and downs over the past months, Baumgartel told us, but this evening was certainly an up.

Since the Congo's independence, economic conditions there had steadily deteriorated, the Congo franc had steadily lost value, and, the Belgian traders having left, vast stocks of certain commodities such as coffee and tea had accumulated inside the stricken land. These, it seems, were now being bartered for much-needed products from outside, such as salt and bottled beer, on a lorry-for-lorry basis. The profits being made by anyone bartering a load of beer for a load of coffee kept trade busy. And not only coffee but gold was being found inside the sacks, gold which was leaving the Congo fast before it slipped from the Belgian miners' hands into those of the authorities. So every lorry, and there were a dozen or more each day, was being searched at the customs post, for this way out of Congo, via Ruanda, was one of the major smuggling routes. This meant a delay of hours or even days for the crews, who seemed to be mainly Italians, and they were thus seeking shelter for the night; Smugglers' Rest might have been a better name for the hotel that night, one felt.

On the subject of gorillas, Baumgartel had sad stories to tell. A fine male had recently been found dead of wounds by Reuben Rwangzire, the chief gorilla guide, and he suspected it was the work of a powerful and bloodthirsty leopard. But far more ominous than this natural disaster, one result of the Congo's independence and the turbulent social changes in Ruanda was that regulations preventing the movement of Ruanda pastoralists from taking their herds up the mountainsides into gorilla country were being ignored successfully for the first time in many years. This encroachment by men and cattle was pushing the lower limit of gorilla habitat further up the mountains daily. And finally Baumgartel suspected that in Ruanda and the Congo, gorillas were being caught, dead or alive, and sold through secret channels to zoos and museums in the civilised world. The net result of all this was that only one group of gorillas now visited the Uganda side

of Muhavura, a group of five, the one which had been seen
that very day. We should have to find this little group of sur-
vivors.

We set off early next morning to make arrangements with
our trackers. We met the great Reuben, but he could not
accompany us as he was off to Entebbe next day to receive a
medal from the governor, on behalf of Her Majesty Queen
Elizabeth, in recognition of his services to wild-life conserva-
tion. He arranged for the two remaining trackers, Peter and
"Muzee," to take us, and provided us with six porters to carry
our gear; we were taking with us a week's stores, and would
camp in Baumgartel's huts on the saddle between Mt. Muhavura and Mt. Mgahinga. Early in the afternoon, amid
wishes of good luck, we set off. Ahead marched the porters
with their loads, while the guides kept us company. It was a
steady slope, but there was a good path and it was less cruel
than the Ruwenzori had been, up above Chapman's Farm.
We were now on a track leading over this mountain saddle
and into Ruanda, a natural pass which had been used for
centuries, most recently by displaced Watutsi fleeing the
wrath of their former Wahutu subjects, who threatened to
cut off the tall men's legs to bring them down to size. Ever-
lasting flowers were common, and as we climbed and the
sounds of humans died away below us we were aware of the
pleasantly bracing air and the over-all silence, as if few birds
and insects lived up here. At ten thousand feet, after a four
thousand-foot climb, we saw the metal and thatch huts of
the camp. We paid off the porters, and started setting up our
gear. Evening came and with it a cold wind. Clouds swept
down from the peak of Muhavura thirty-five hundred feet
above us; we grew desperately cold. We tried lighting a fire in
our hut but the smoke was so thick we had to crouch at floor
level in order to breathe; our eyes streamed and our throats
pricked, and then that was no use. The three men (two trackers and a camp guard) must have spotted our antics, for in

no time they had made a fire out in the open, a big blazing bonfire, and put a couple of wicker screens on the windward side of it; sitting inside those screens we toasted ourselves as the night closed in around us. And when at last we plunged out into the cold and made for our camp-beds we kept on all our clothes inside a feather-filled sleeping bag, covered with a thick blanket, and still our feet were cold.

The next morning was dank and misty and we could not see downwards into the plains at all, or upwards to Muhavura. We set off about 8 A.M. and first the guides led us downwards along a steep track through the bamboo forest, which here covers the mountain in a broad horizontal belt around the ten thousand-foot contour. At nine-thirty we picked up the track of two days ago—a flattened trail left by these enormous heavy creatures as they move slowly along, with dung at intervals along it and the occasional bamboo peelings. We now began a similar kind of journey to that described by Alan Moorehead, up the near vertical sides of gulleys, along ridges, down again into a gulley, for this is a jagged volcanic cone, with longitudinal fissures running downwards from the summit. As we toiled along we heard golden monkeys but could not see them in the dense bamboo, saw droppings which could have been leopard, and bigger ones, though not at all fresh, of elephant. Elephant here? Yes, they assured us, elephants sometimes climbed to the very summit of Muhavura. Well, if an elephant could do it then so could we.

At ten-thirty, while still in the bamboo, we came across the gorillas' sleeping place of the previous night, four nests close to each other in the tops of bamboos, and one nearby on the ground which must have belonged to the old male; as we expected, it contained dung. Now we emerged from the bamboo into a landscape, none the less jagged, of giant *lobelia* and *senecio*, where we continued sliding and slipping down, and heaving ourselves up on roots and tufts of grass which naturally came out half the time so that we had to start

again. We were by now rather dead, I fear, to the skilful tracking which was keeping us on the gorillas' path; at times we
wondered whether we could hope to catch up with them, our
progress was so slow. But the trackers were confident.

After three and a half hours of following, Peter suddenly
signed us to listen and we heard a crack as a branch was
snapped ahead of us. We scrambled higher and peered into the
gulley ahead, and there on the opposite side below us we saw
a splendid black gorilla looking at us. It watched us a while
and then went on feeding and moved up the side of the gulley
opposite looking like a great black bear. Then came another
from the bottom, this one a female with a baby on her back.
She, too, looked at us, transferred the baby to her belly, and
pulled herself up and out of sight behind the foliage. Next
came the big male, a huge gorilla with a silver back. He looked
at us and roared and barked at us angrily over the gulley. Then
he went up a little way until he was hidden and must have
stayed there and watched us all the time for he still barked,
roared, and beat his chest from time to time, making a strange
hollow knocking sound and also slapping and thudding noises.
While this was going on, two more smaller gorillas came into
view and both walked up the same route slowly, after having
a good look at us.

Altogether we had been watching for half an hour and
were conscious of our extreme good luck. As the minutes had
been ticking by we had felt something of the grandeur of
these giants in their mountain fastness, but more the extreme
aloofness of them; the male had conveyed his power to us,
and the rest had shown themselves to be curious and dignified.
Also, we had established for sure that there was a baby in
the group, perhaps two years old, making the total number
six. We had been exceptionally well placed for observation:
above the gorillas and at a good distance from them. We now
started the return to camp, exhausted but elated by our success at the first attempt. Peter explained to us that the go-

rillas were now going up the mountain; he doubted whether we would see them again.

Nevertheless, the next morning found us on those jagged slopes again, crawling up and up, far higher than we had been the day before, up until we reached the new nesting site, four in the trees and one below as on the previous night. Up the track went, headed apparently straight for the summit of Mu- havura. This was an advantage: we were moving along a ridge without having to cross gulleys all the time. Up and up we went, out of the senecio zone and into a higher one of giant heather—small gaunt trees with bilious-looking lichen hanging from the branches in streamers—steadily step by step picking our way along the ridge under a blue sky with only one cloud forming around the summit, now a mere two thousand feet above us. At eleven twenty-five the trackers heard feeding noises; we went on a few steps and immediately the silence of the mountain, so far this morning broken only by the dull slow padding of our feet and our panting breaths, was shat- tered by a terrible roar, long and furious like a mad dog's, and we heard a thump as of rapidly approaching pelting feet. Ahead of me the two trackers turned and ran back down the mountain. I, too, turned and shouted to Frankie to run down; we all four tumbled down the mountain with extreme haste and no grace and came to rest below by a big rock, whereupon we all burst out laughing with relief. Not even Peter, who was in the lead, had seen the big male as he charged; probably he hadn't stopped to look. We remembered now, objectively, that this charge of the gorilla is no more than a display, rarely leading to attack, so that one can in fact stand still and watch it. On this occasion the combination of surprise, shock, and an instinct in all of us telling us strongly to get out of it had triumphed. But then we recalled that this par- ticular gruff old male was known to attack by throttling and had twice got hold of Reuben in this way, and I for one was glad we had been cowards enough to run.

Above us the cloud still lingered around Muhavura's volcanic rim and silence reigned absolute in the mountain air; below, the sun was on the mountain slopes, and among the ridges of greens and browns we saw a tiny silver speck: our own camp; three hours later when we returned the guard greeted us with relief—he had heard the roar more than a mile away over the trees.

That afternoon we sent him down to Kisoro to summon the porters; we had accomplished our objective and now saw that the gorillas were moving out of range. Up they would go, over the mountain's shoulder and down into Ruanda on the far side. If only we could have warned them of the dangers across the border! Next evening we were telling Baumgartel all we had seen, and the day after that were on our way north, through the Impenetrable Forest, the only spot in Uganda where both gorillas and chimpanzees are known to occur. And as we bumped around the precipitous tree-covered gulleys of this forest on the one road which cuts through it, we imagined the two species around us among the trees and got back to thinking about those striking differences which had puzzled us.

There was the difference in food habits, and we now saw the importance of one specific point. The gorilla can find its food almost anywhere—it spends more time deciding which of the available foods growing all around it to eat, than where to find any food at all. This is because pithy stems, roots, etc., are found scattered about everywhere. What is more, they are available everywhere all the year round. Gorillas thus feed, as we saw them do, by working their way in a compact group along a rather imprecise route at a slow pace, eating a little here and a little there as they go. When they do make special journeys to particular feeding areas, it is because the food in these areas is preferable, not because there is no food elsewhere. For the fruit-eating chimpanzee this is not the case: we had been struck by the overwhelming importance of the whereabouts of ripe fruits in determining the pattern of movement and distribution of the Budongo chimpanzees. They had a flexible social organisation because they needed it in order to be able to exploit the fruit supply, now concentrated in one spot, now scattered all over the forest. Whereas, in theory, gorillas *could* go around as chimps do, there is no advantage to be gained in doing so. Indeed, one can see the advantage of being in a group with a big male leader to provide protection—an advantage which chimpanzees have had to forego completely. This, then, was how food habits had helped to shape the social organisation of each species.

Then there was the fact that the gorilla was quiet and the chimpanzee vociferous. Apart from the terrifying roar and the barking and chest-beating of the adult male, the gorillas we had seen, and those described by Schaller, were quiet animals with a number of subdued vocalisations. In other words, noise is the gorilla's technique of threatening an enemy, and is largely the prerogative of the adult male. There is none of the wild chorusing of chimpanzees, whose hullaballoo is not primarily threat behaviour, but, we thought, could well be a distance signal enabling chimpanzees all over the forest to home on good food sources. Now after our trip it was obvious to us that gorillas would have no use for such noisy chorusing, there being no special areas of good food. A fascinating detail drove home to us the importance of vocalisations in chimpanzees as opposed to gorillas: the chimp's ears are much bigger for its size and stick out much further from the head than the gorilla's.

The temperamental difference between the two species also now seemed to be a logical one and to fall into the general framework. Gorillas travel along slowly, they rarely get excited or worked up about anything. Chimpanzees, in contrast, move along the forest floor at a great pace; the males in particular cover more ground each day than do gorillas; they hoot and drum as they move along, and when they find a fruiting tree their enthusiasm knows no bounds. This kind of boisterous behaviour could only be exhibited by a species with an underlying "volatile" temperament and this is the way chimpanzee temperament has evolved; gorillas, on the other hand, have never stood to gain from excitability in everyday life; their temperament has thus become placid and their only expression of excitement comes in their threatening displays.

But what about the dung? What explanation could we find in terms of temperament or social organisation or food habits? Wasn't it just that the gorilla was a slothful, dirty creature, while the chimpanzee had developed a primitive toilet sense? Why look further into this rather messy problem? Why muck about with dung? We couldn't help it. When we had found the gorillas' nesting site, on our first day, we had been struck not by the pile of dung in the big male's ground nest, which we had expected, but by the fact that, although pushed down by the weight of his body (some three hundred to four hundred pounds), it still retained its basic shape. Thinking back to the gorillas we had seen, I remembered them as clean-looking, glossy-haired animals. And Schaller in his book remarked on the fact that gorillas are not dirtied by lying on their dung. With chimpanzees it is different. Their food is less fibrous and so their droppings are soft, loose, and often messy. If chimpanzees lay in their dung all night it would cling to their fur and act as a focus of infection. So, in the course of chimpanzee evolution, natural selection may well have favoured those with hygienic habits and eliminated those with unhygienic ones, while gorillas have been more fortunate—despite their apparently dirty habits, their diet makes it difficult for them to be unhygienic!

So we theorised as we drove the long journey back to Bunyoro. The road jogged us mercilessly along every hot hour, our equipment clattered around in the back of the Land Rover, attractive hills or dull flat landscapes passed slowly by on either side; on the second day we were forced to a stand-still by a great storm which blotted out everything for half an hour and left the red road steaming ahead of us. Steadily we made our way northwards, to Fort Portal and beyond, and were back on our beloved verandah by nightfall of the second day, with the welcoming calls of chimpanzees in our ears.

CHAPTER TEN

Back to Budongo

Before we broke our study to go to the gorillas, we had seen four seasons go by, the fig, lean, ngrube, and igeria seasons. We had obtained excellent evidence that chimpanzees did not live in permanent groups, and we had developed certain theories about the nature of chimp society and the function of the choruses. But, and we felt this keenly, we had not yet obtained satisfactory data relating to the problem of *which* chimpanzees went *where*, i.e. whether or not a particular number of chimps, however loosely bound together, occupied a given area of forest only and did all their wandering around in it. Such an area, known as a "range," is very common in animals of all kinds, and we suspected that ranges existed for our chimpanzees too, as we most often heard them in certain areas and more rarely in others. But since we lacked proof of which chimpanzees were in fact calling in these areas we could not be sure of whether they kept to ranges or not. Of one thing we were sure, namely that the ranges, if they existed, were very large, for there were no small, compact areas of a square mile or so where chimpanzees could be found at all times. When one species of fruit tree ripened they were feeding on this; when it was replaced by another in a different part of the forest they moved accordingly. So the range, if it

existed, must be extensive enough to contain a number of
trees of each major food species in order to provide a year-
round supply of food.

While we had been away in Kigezi, we had formulated in
rough a plan of campaign which ought to help us get the
necessary facts to answer our outstanding problem. On returning to the forest we would hire some of the wandering un-
employed in our region to be "chimp-spotters"—about six of
them, we thought; these would be placed at strategic listening points and their daily reports should give us a clearer picture of the *total* pattern of movement of all the chimpanzees
in our study area. For our major difficulty to date had been
that by following one group we were forced to neglect and
lose track of all the others; we should now have several pairs
of ears and eyes in the forest like a network of survey posts,
and we should, in theory at least, be able to track several chimpanzee movements without actually following any of them.
So now, back in Budongo, we began putting out feelers
among the local people to try and get some good chimp-spotters, and in this Manueri helped a good deal.

Meantime we planned to continue jungle-bashing as usual.
July was now well advanced and, although we did not know it
yet, a new season had begun; gone forever were our days in
the Siba swamps. The first thing we noticed on our return
was the extraordinary loudness of the calling, which seemed
to be coming from the forest just below the house. All our
first evening at home it continued; were they welcoming us
back? Looking down towards the noisy forest next morning
at dawn, we were staggered to find the tree-tops we knew so
well full of chimpanzees; I still remember the strange feeling
of standing, snake-bite serum in pocket, camera and binoculars slung, Manueri at my side with his panga, bag packed
full of sandwiches, water, and plastic macs, anxious to get
back on the trail after our break, only to be faced with this

unpredicted turn of events: we could now do our observing from the verandah!

Manueri, despite his fortnight's holiday, was quick off the mark. "Sisi nakwenda, soko-mutu nakuja," he laughed—"We go away, the chimpanzees come," adding seriously, "Mimi nafikiri, kama sisi nafuta-futa kibirani, yote tatoroka mbale sana"—"I think that if we go down and search for them in the forest, they will all flee a long way away." I nodded in agreement with his second point; we should certainly find out less by going down the hill and hacking our way in to these chimpanzees than by staying put. For the first time I got out the 60 × magnification telescope lent us by Dollonds of London, and mounted it on the verandah. Manueri hung around for a bit, politely, but was soon up in his hut lying on his back and smoking—the halcyon days had come. We took notes and watched.

Below the house we distinguished, with the telescope, four adult males feeding together in one tree and in another a mixed group of seven chimpanzees of all ages and sexes. The trees were musisi or *Maesopsis*, the colonising species of Budongo. We had read in a book by Eggeling that this species was a favourite food of the chimpanzee but had never, so far, found them in it. Now we could see that each tree with chimps was festooned with thousands of tiny yellow or black fruits, depending on the state of ripeness, while other nearby trees were still unripe and covered in blobs of green. Perhaps Eggeling had watched them on these very trees from the spot where we were now standing, when he had lived here.

We kept our things ready to go down if they disappeared, but they stayed. As always, new chimps came and others left. Our four males were, we felt sure, a group we had seen together on previous occasions, and which we called the "royal clan" because they were so relaxed; this group seemed to be more permanent than most chimpanzee groups, although we could not be sure whether the four stayed together all the time; they might split up and meet again. By now we were ensconced in camp-chairs with our feet on the table and bush-jackets abandoned for cooler clothes, with Semei laughingly turning up with mugs of tea at regular intervals. Information of all sorts was pouring in. For a start, we saw one of our males make a "day-bed" at mid-morning and settle down on his back in it for a snooze—he appeared not to go to sleep but simply to want a rest, for he lay there yawning and stretching in the sunshine (the nest was right at the top of a tree), and after an hour or so of this, got up quite casually and left. In addition, from our new position above canopy level we could see anything from five to a dozen chimpanzees at the same time and observe their interactions with each other as, one by one, they stopped feeding and either left the tree or started to groom one another. We saw a big old grey-backed male, so old his face was lean and showed the skull beneath, grooming and being groomed by a spry young female having an early estrus. We watched them groom each other, and then the grooming stopped; the old male collected a few branches underneath him for comfort, and sat gazing into space over the tree-tops, his young lady seemingly forgotten. She sat nearby scratching, and nibbling a desultory bite of fruit here and there, then walked away.

These chimpanzees called from time to time, their wild music going out over the trees and provoking a response from other groups deeper in the forest. For all of one day we re-corded every call, its time, the direction it came from, whether or not there was any drumming; from this information we were able to plot groups of chimps moving down among the trees as the bearing of their calls crept degree by degree across the compass dial. We got better evidence than ever before for our theory that the calling of chimpanzees feeding busily up aloft acts as both a magnet and a beacon for wandering groups of chimpanzees in the forest below.

By late morning our males had left for pastures new, but some of the others were still there. We lunched to their sporadic music. In the afternoon they moved slowly to neighbouring trees where we could still see them; it was wonderful to be able to watch their agility in the branches, unhurried and yet powerful and fast, bending the smaller branches under them, climbing tree-trunks that rose vertically for a hundred feet with an ease which really brought home to us what it is to be a chimpanzee, to look around one at ground level and see the world not, human-fashion, as a number of paths *between* the trees, but as a number of paths *up* the trees; and, once up aloft, to see each tree-crown nearby as a field of branches in which to wander and pluck the choicest fruits.

For three days there were nearly always some chimps visible from our verandah; sometimes, too, blue monkeys and red-tails came to feed on the musisis with them. The tree-tops where they fed were now beginning to look ravaged with hundreds of broken-off branch-stubs and dying leaves, and we got a good idea of the way in which chimpanzees help the spread of the *Maesopsis* tree, by depositing the stones (in their dung) in areas far from the parent tree, as they wander through the forest. Other species of animals also help the *Maesopsis* spread—the hornbills, the duikers, and the civet, for instance. But of these only the hornbills move regularly over such long distances as the chimpanzees, and they probably drop their stones before going far, which makes the chimpanzee the number-one distributor of *Maesopsis* trees in the forest and ought, therefore, to make him the forester's friend, since *Maesopsis* is a valuable timber tree. But the forester is ungrateful, and is at the present time engaged in a systematic attempt to kill off all the fig-trees in the forest by a massive tree-poisoning programme, since figs do not make good timber; in so doing he will strike a blow at the chimpanzees, which rely on figs during part of the year; it is a blow which they may survive, being highly adaptable creatures, but only in reduced numbers. They will have lost their favourite food, the mukunyu, and will have to try and find substitutes during certain months. Let us hope substitutes are available, for no-one knows.

We fully acknowledge Uganda's need to continue timber production; in an underdeveloped country there can be no talk of wild-life survival where the survival of essential industries is at stake. And yet, is it really necessary to kill off the figs in order to benefit the mahoganies? According to Eggeling, figs contribute greatly to soil fertility. While nothing is proved, it is possible to suggest that the forest as a whole, and therefore the mahoganies, might suffer if fig-trees were exterminated. But whether that is true or not, there is no doubt about the importance of figs to the chimpanzees. The Forest Department is watching to see the effects tree-poisoning will have on chimpanzees, but it will be very difficult for anyone not engaged full-time on the task to notice a decline in their numbers. In the meantime, every day, more trees in Budongo are being pumped with a mixture of diesel oil and a hormone killer which prevents proper cell growth; *no-one* knows what the full effects of this poisoning programme will be on the wild life which at present abounds around the trees and on them and underneath them. What we need are censuses of the numbers of animals living in areas which have been poisoned; the figures can then be compared with those for unpoisoned areas of the same forest type. Let us hope that such work will be started before the balance of plant and animal life in whole areas of forest is irrevocably upset.

Getting back to the season of the musisis and to our verandah, there was a quiet spell after the third day, with no chimps, and we had evidence from our notebooks that throughout these three days they had been moving off towards the south. We began trekking through the forest again. It was strange, they had disappeared. We followed along the rim of the Budongo Forest and came to the place where the

main road cuts between the Budongo and the Siba. Here Manueri found fresh chimp tracks crossing the main road. We
entered the Siba from this new direction on Manueri's hy-
pothesis. And there, in the afternoon, we heard chimpanzees
calling, miles away, deep in the distant Siba, in the elephant-
ridden part. If these were our chimpanzees they could stay
there; we would look for some different ones. And for a few
days we did. Then one dawn there was calling from the south
of Busingiro, loud strident calling like the yelping of wild
dogs; these were excited chimpanzees. We went down into the
forest and headed towards the music, which was almost continuous. We soon realised that they were coming towards
us and coming fast. Drumming in great rolls reverberated
through the trees and every instant we expected to see a black
form in the bushes, see it pull up sharp and look at us and
dive off again into the darkness. The noise was now growing
fantastically loud and we could scarcely believe that it could
get louder, but it could and did. We began to feel that if this
enormous horde of approaching chimpanzees did bump into
us it would be just too bad for us—they sounded utterly
lunatic in their extreme frenzy of drumming and hooting. We
stopped still by a tree-trunk; I comforted Frankie as best I
could and Manueri peered forwards with panga at the ready.

All of a sudden we realised that they were passing by us.
We could have shouted out loud and not made ourselves
heard above the din; a few times something moved between
the saplings but the noise of their voices was so great that we
heard no footsteps or rustling leaves. For a minute or two
this phenomenon, like a cyclone or a passing express train,
swept past us and then was gone, travelling north. We looked
at each other in bewilderment; none of us had so much as
glimpsed a chimpanzee, only seen the bushes moving everywhere. As before with the gorillas, we laughed and spoke out
loudly in our relief after the awful mounting tension and
terrible climax. One thing we had learnt: that the howling

of a mob of chimpanzees, whatever functions it may have in the organising of chimp society, is extremely intimidating to other species in its path. This helped to answer a problem we had often wondered about: why chimpanzees were so keen to announce their whereabouts to all and sundry, including leopards. It now seemed to us that any leopard caught in a mob of chimps as we had been, would be more likely to retreat terrified into a crotch than risk a plunge into that cauldron of screaming fury. Another mystery was cleared up too— how it was that we had in the past been able to hear chimpanzees over vast distances, which we had measured up to two full miles as the crow flies: we now felt that the noise we had heard, produced as it was by the combined lung power of some twenty or more chimpanzees, would carry a couple of miles with no trouble at all. Problem: what in heaven's name were they up to?

During the week after our return I had interviewed at least a dozen men, to select those who, I felt, were the best type for the job of chimp-spotting, for our new large-scale attack on the problem of chimp ranges. After establishing that they knew what chimpanzees and their calls were like, by asking for an imitation (which most of the men were glad to provide), and weeding out those who lived too far away or whom Manueri disapproved of, I had selected six men who, starting next Monday, were to be at certain fixed spots—"strategic points" on chimpanzee routes or between areas thought by us to be possible chimp ranges—to keep their ears and eyes open for three hours after dawn and again for three hours before dusk, and report to us when we came to visit them on anything they might have seen or heard. It was ambitious stuff, and this, our first attempt at such a project in the heart of Africa, failed utterly; within the week we had fired every man. Not a single one of them consistently turned up on time or in the right place, when it rained they didn't come, or their bicycles let them down, or something. But word had got around about what we were looking for, and soon men were turning up on Busingiro Hill in a steady stream, presenting themselves for the jobs. Having learnt a few lessons from the first batch, I now enquired whether they were afraid of the forest, whether they minded being left alone in the forest for three hours, what they would do in the rain, did they want an advance? (If yes, I told them to go home.) It took time, but we ended up with four reliable men. They all had one quality in common—an extreme aloofness and independence of spirit, born, most probably, of prolonged suffering.

There was Zachariah, tall and lean with a domed, professorial head, a quiet-spoken man with a keen sense of fun, if you caught what he said. The second, Akijero, had left his wife and child in Hoima and was wandering around Bunyoro asking for work; he had been away for three months and this was the first job he had found. Third was Amis, the sacked houseboy of a local European; he claimed to be an expert cook but according to his reference (which he could not read) was a kitchen-boy and a bad one. The last was a smiling-faced, pock-marked local who lived on his own and went under the extraordinary name of Watu Hapana, which means "no people": he certainly was lacking entirely in the social instinct, but claimed the name had been given him at birth and not as a result of his behaviour. This, then, was the force with which we hoped to breach the final mystery of the chimpanzees, the problem of how big their "tribes" were and how far the range of each tribe extended. Amis and Zachariah and Akijero came to live with Semei and Manueri; Watu Hapana stayed at home, until he took to the job so warmly that he built himself a little hut at his allocated observation point, after which he worked twelve hours a day and became a fanatical source of information about the chimpanzees' latest movements and positions: he may have been "no people" but he certainly was "chimp."

We were now obliged to make visits to our men at 10 A.M.

and at 6:30 P.M. for their reports, and so for a while the old routine of jungle-bashing came to an end and a new one took its place. During the period before 10 A.M. and between 11 A.M. and the evening we now followed up any groups of chimpanzees located by the men or, if none seemed promising, stationed ourselves at a fifth observation point for the day, using the time available to work on our maps and plot the latest information. Akijero was walking up Track A as far as R.P.5, Amis was at the first river on the mill track, Zachariah was half a mile along Track B, Watu Hapana was down by the Siba swamps, we ourselves observed from the road at the Budongo-Siba crossing point. We had the study area in our grip, sixteen square miles of forest in which we ought to be able to pick up any noisy chimpanzee group, locate it, and follow its progress.

In addition to our work of watching and analysing data as we sat at the roadside, we were kept busy greeting and replying to passing Africans, for this is no land of the curtly civil "good morning" or "good afternoon" and the false smile. The ritual, repeated with every man and woman who came padding or cycling up the road went something like this:

"Jambo"—"Hullo."

"Jambo."

"Habari?"—"What news?"

"Muzuri. Habari?"—"Good news. What is your news?"

"Muzuri tu"—"Only good."

"Poli kazi"—"Work slowly."

"Poli poli"—"Go steadily."

"Eh"—"Yes."

"Mmmm."

"Mmmm." (Out of earshot now.)

All spoken in quiet, sedate tones, fading with the last "mmmm" into the African silence. There were variations on the ceremony; for instance, enquiry might be made, after "Muzuri tu," as to our success in hearing chimpanzees, or we could enquire where a man was going, or whence he had come, or if his fish was for sale. If there was any conversation, one ended with "Kwaheri" (Good-bye).

The soft tones of the Africans' voices in greeting somehow conveyed the tranquillity of their lives; more than this, the complacent way the long ritual was delivered expressed their whole fatalistic approach to life, and the steady pad-padding of their feet on the red road drove this impression home. Here was none of the white man's dash and verve; here was no belief in progress; here, one felt, was life balanced in perfect equilibrium with the earth, and the earth might even be no more than a symbol of death.

Then, always, just as our minds were musing on imponderable things, lulled no doubt by the heat and the constant drone of insects in the trees, a black form would emerge at the roadside thirty yards away—the head of a chimpanzee, standing on its hind legs to peer over the grass and make sure it was safe to cross. Look left, look right, look left again, then cross—but wait a minute, this chimp has disappeared. It turns out he was scared of us, for in a minute he reappears a hundred yards further off, crossing the road at a steady walk, his head turned to look at us; in the middle of the road he stops, stands upright for a moment or two to gaze at us, then goes on to the far side and vanishes into a little hole in the forest edge. He is following a well-marked chimp track. Now two others cross behind him, a female and an adolescent, then after a moment another female, all looking at us as they go. None makes any sound. We write everything down in the notebook: time of crossing, direction they crossed, sex and age of each individual, special characteristics. Then back to waiting again. Now we hear chorusing distantly in the Siba, whence the chimpanzees we saw just now have come—there are many more left behind: will they follow later? The calling is answered by hoots from the Budongo side, perhaps from our chimps but probably not as the calls are too far away;

probably they came from chimps which crossed earlier in the
morning; or perhaps a new group is moving up from deep inside the Budongo, ready to cross back in a few hours time.

During these weeks spent road-watching we saw hundreds
of chimps cross, often the same ones time and time again.
As they went they showed themselves to be bold or timid,
curious or indifferent, well-built or skinny (none were fat).
One mother crossed carrying two babies, the smaller under
her belly, the larger on her back, while an even larger third
one trailed close behind her. Africans did not seem bothered
by the chimps when they met them on the road, nor did the
chimps bother about the Africans; it was fascinating to see
this crossing of the ways, the road being an artery of com-
munications for humans, driven straight as a die through an
arm of inhospitable forest, while for the chimps this red gash
of gravel was an obstacle to their easy progress through the
friendly tangle of greens and browns. Only once did we see
chimps make use of the road as humans do; it was the "royal
clan." The big male appeared first, stepping out on his powerful hands, looking left and right, seeing us, deciding we were
harmless, and then beginning to walk *towards* us along the
road! As he stepped off, he was followed in single file by the
remaining three males in this band—two large and one small.
They now ambled along the road towards us, their movements beautifully supple and relaxed, looking around and
behind themselves occasionally, but mostly looking at us. Relentlessly the leader male came on; we wondered how close he
would come. He paused, and they paused behind him. Then,
as if by common agreement, they stepped aside, clambered
up the roadside bank, and went into their home, the leader
stopping a while in the grass on the bank to study us before he
disappeared.

So we passed the days, and they went surprisingly quickly,
considering that all we were doing was sitting by the road-

☷ Much frequented patches of *Maesopsis*
▢ Forest │ ▦ Bush
↙ Directions of most frequent
  chimpanzee movements

Fig. 6. During the *Maesopsis* season, food within our study area
was concentrated in the big patches of *Maesopsis* trees shown
above. Chimpanzees moved in the directions indicated by arrows,
gathering in large numbers on the fruiting trees.

side. We plotted calls and crossings on our maps, and built up
a fair idea of the distribution of chimpanzees in our immediate area, and every evening we got the reports of our men, so
we were able to make quite a wide survey. And though the
chimps made it as hard for us as they could, by moving in un-

predictable directions (or rather, against our predictions), we
began to get some idea of what was going on.

The pattern which emerged was one of chimpanzees concentrated in large numbers in the *Maesopsis* patches, whose
location we knew from our Forest Department maps. These
Maesopsis patches were mostly around the edges of the forest,
but sometimes deep inside, and, where the forest was growing
rapidly, were sometimes several acres in extent. Within these
areas we now, on our trips into the forest, found larger gather-
ings of chimpanzees than we had hitherto imagined possible,
and although we could never see them all, we calculated that
over fifty animals might be concentrated in an acre or two of
Maesopsis. Of these, small sub-groups would split off after the
morning feed and go roaming, and either we ourselves or our
men would frequently see these wanderers, adults mainly, and
often just males, crossing tracks on their way to another part
of the forest for the day, returning to the *Maesopsis* during
the late afternoon for the evening feed. They travelled in
groups of half a dozen or so, called often as they went, and
doubtless listened carefully to those left behind. Mothers and
their totos were rarely to be found in these travelling groups.

And then, inevitably, reported by each of our men in turn,
came the phenomenon we had been caught up in ourselves on
that day early in the season: the mass movement. First Amis
reported it, he had seen *many* chimpanzees ("mingi *mingi*"),
thirty or forty of them; they had come thundering up along
his valley (which we knew was a traditional chimp route with
well-worn tracks) and had made their way northwards with
an enormous uproar; we cursed ourselves for not having been
there to see and count them, but Amis was clear on one point:
he had seen many mothers and babies with the group. Then
Watu Hapana reported the same story, he had counted
twenty-three chimpanzees crossing the road, making a mark in
the ground for each one with his stick; they had all crossed
within the space of an hour; we cursed again, but there was

no way short of walkie-talkie for responding to these situations as they arose.

Not all the chimpanzees were moving around in such large numbers together. One mass movement which we ourselves watched, from the Siba to the Budongo, which followed a stay lasting over a fortnight by large numbers of chimps in a single big *Maesopsis* patch in the Siba, took place in dribs and drabs over two full days; on this occasion seventeen mothers, each with an infant, six childless females, ten young, and thirteen adult males were seen; in addition to these we had probably missed the forerunners of the move, adult males most likely, since these were already calling ahead when we first arrived to watch. Allowing for these and others we had missed during the two days through not having eyes at the back of our heads, a total of seventy to eighty animals may have crossed.

At the same time we were getting very clear evidence from our co-workers that absolutely no boundaries could be drawn where chimpanzees never crossed from one area into another; small groups were always to be found on the move, crossing every river and track. On the other hand, there were three regions within the study area, each about eight square miles in extent, within each of which chimpanzees were normally to be found, and had been found by us during all the previous months and seasons of our study. We were now able to determine that when a good patch of musisi was attracting chimpanzees to the Siba, it attracted sixty to eighty animals but did not attract the Kamirambwa chimps, which could be heard by Amis in a musisi patch at the edge of the forest near the river; and it did not attract the Bubwe River chimps, which we knew from Akijero to be feeding on the musisi patch behind the Game Department huts down below Busingiro. We concluded from this that while each region of six to eight square miles contained sixty to eighty chimpanzees which lived in that region and were able to find within that region a year-round food supply, nevertheless some of these individuals, mainly the adult males and some females, did move freely from one region to another.

As the year had gone by and different species of trees had fruited, different parts of each region had been the focus of the chimpanzees' attention, but we knew each region to contain a sufficiency of every fruit tree utilised by the chimpanzees, and so we had no reason to suppose that the *bulk* of the population of one region would ever leave it and go to another. A simple but very crude analogy can be drawn with humans living in, say, London and Manchester: each city provides its population with their requirements all the year round, and the bulk of the population is always present in its home city; nevertheless there is continual coming and going between the two. The analogy would be more exact if Londoners, in their search for food, had to spend a month in East Ham (all of them!), a couple of months in Hampstead, a fortnight scattered widely over the whole of the Greater London area, finally converging on, say, Hyde Park for two glorious months, to spread out again along the Edgware Road, Oxford Street, Bayswater Road, and down into Kensington as the pattern of food distribution changed once more, while in Manchester similar events were taking place. But with chimpanzees at ten to the square mile, and city-folk at forty-two to the acre, this analogy should not be taken too seriously.

Getting back to the chimpanzees, we now felt we had the answer to the problem of ranges. Our evidence indicated that such ranges *did* exist for chimps, and that in fact, as far as the chimps were concerned, there is a home-range consisting of an area of some six to eight or more square miles of forest, beyond which the ground is less familiar. Within this home-range live some seventy or so chimpanzees all of whom, doubtless, know each other (and many of whom must be related to each other). Of these, the aged, the mothers, and the younger children probably do not leave the home-range very often, whereas adult males and some adult females do leave it from time to time and on these occasions, when a number of them meet up with another group, "carnivals" take place.

Having established the approximate size and number of inhabitants of the ranges, we were in a position to calculate the total chimp population of the forest. In our area they were about ten to the square mile. The Budongo Forest has an area of 135 square miles, added to which are the 35 square miles of the Siba. If the density of chimps in our area was typical, there would be some 1700 chimps in the whole forest. But we knew there were vast areas of ironwood forest in the north-east of Budongo, and here chimp density would probably be lower. On the other hand, there were some elephant-ridden parts of the Siba where we felt it might be higher. Conclusion: at a safe guess there were between 1000 and 2000 chimpanzees in the forest.

The *Maesopsis* season was glorious and long, it went on all through August and up to mid-September. As it faded and our big clusters of chimpanzees fractured into smaller units, we began to feel that we had accomplished something of what we had set out to do. We had bad days even then, days when not a chimpanzee was heard by any of the men, days when we went in, searching for an elusive band which led us through swamps and even through grassland, tall and dry and ready to burn. But by mid-September we and the men were already talking about "Uhuru" (Freedom)—Independence Day for Uganda, October 9, was coming up fast—and about the end of our study, the last pay-day, which would follow shortly after. For, despite a generous gift from the Wilkie Foundation of the United States, supplementing our University of London grant, we were already running short of money and knew that the next month would have to be our last. We wanted badly to stay a full year, but there just wasn't the money to do it.

And, as if the forest knew our predicament and wanted to comfort us, it began to throw out figs once again on every mukunyu tree. During our last month, October, there developed a repetition of the scene with which we were so familiar from the February before, of mixed groups of a dozen or so chimpanzees clustered on single ripe fruiting fig-trees. It was the start of a new fig season, we were certain of that; figs of all sorts were ripening as well as the mukunyu; there was the mukunyu number two, the mukunyu number three, a whole range of nyakatomas, and other figs besides. Time pressed inexorably on and the bank balance dwindled, our men had to be paid and the bill for the precious knowledge we had gained was cruelly high. Did depression set in? How could it, with Uhuru just a week away?

October 9, 1962: Independence Day for Uganda. We were rounding off our research in the forest, saying good-bye to the trees and tracks and chimpanzees.

During the preceding weeks I had discussed Independence with Manueri and Semei. To Manueri I had jokingly said, "On October 9 you will be the 'bwana' and I the servant; you will have to pay me wages," which had tickled him no end. With Semei it was rather different; he took Independence seriously and was genuinely glad to see the white rule go, but he understood that some white men were good for Uganda because they brought her money and trade; he thought, too, that the Uganda government should now try to loosen the Indian grip on commerce and allow the Africans to take over slowly. Manueri was old and knew things never change; as long as he could work and buy waragi it didn't matter who the government was. Semei was young and full of ambitions, not only for himself but for his country. Maybe he will be a politician one day.

With the Congo so close at hand, and in view of the large number of Congolese immigrants working at the mill and wandering around, we were naturally anxious lest Independence should be an occasion for recriminations against the white community. We had asked Africans what their attitude to us would be after Independence, and they had unanimously expressed the desire to keep us on; they were always courteous and joked with us; and in truth we had no colonialist tradition to embitter them, for Uganda has always been considered a "black man's land" and colonials going to East Africa had mostly gone to Kenya. Thus very few whites own land in Uganda; most are in government service, education, or business.

Yet many of the Europeans working at the sawmill had had experience of Mau Mau, and the Congo memory was fresh in our minds. How would the Africans react to Uhuru once their reasoning was befuddled with drink? And drink they would; all of them were eagerly looking forward to *days*, not hours, at the pombe barrel. As it happened, we were not the only ones worrying about this problem: so were the local African chiefs. And they issued a directive to every man in their jurisdiction that if there was any trouble those responsible would be for it; to make doubly sure, they directed that no Africans were to move around during the drunken days, Sunday, Monday, and Uhuru Day, Tuesday. Manueri and Semei told us they might be late returning for work, since they would be unable to set out until it was safe for them to walk the roads again. We gave them some "Uhuru" meat for the long weekend.

During these Freedom days we Europeans were as homebound as the Africans themselves, having no-one to look after the place if we went out, and no great desire to go anywhere. Frankie and I gazed out over the forest from our verandah; the historic time arrived and passed by; it rained and the shadows of clouds passed over the trees. The sun shone again.

In fact, the passing of Independence was without incident in the whole of Uganda. Indeed, except for the celebrations

organised by the various authorities and in a few big commercial undertakings, Independence came as a giant binge,
and passed off as an outsize hangover. We had given our men
the whole of Wednesday off in case the roads were not yet
clear, but midway through the day Manueri returned saying
he thought he'd better get out of it and come back to us or
he would die of liquor. Semei likewise had a tale of much
drinking to tell.

The biggest celebrations were in Kampala, where a stadium
had been constructed and a huge crowd watched the tattoo,
with African dancing and highly organised numbers from each
part of the country; in the evening the town went gay. Union
Jacks everywhere came down sedately and were replaced by
the new national emblem: a crested crane in a circle on a
striped black, gold, and red background. Everywhere one
sensed the presence of an ambiguous formality; was it a hoax?
What was freedom? Would the Baganda now start their tyr-
anny? Would Europeans leave and jobs be fewer? There was
a slogan we often heard: "Uhuru parmoja"—"Freedom together"; I think that most thinking men in Uganda at that
time were a little afraid that in gaining independence they
would lose those few benefits the white man had brought:
free hospitals, an end to inter-tribal war, some jobs, and a
working system of education. As it happened, nothing
changed drastically in our up-country district of Bunyoro, and
while no Africans suffered from the new regime, we saw few
who had benefited. Those few were an extreme minority re-
placing white men in official positions, a process which had
been going on for some time before Independence and which
continues at the present day.

So Uhuru came to a finish on Wednesday night and on
Thursday we were out again for our last few days of jungle-
bashing. Time was against us now and yet we could not hurry:
it would have spoilt the harmony. The sunrise was the same,
and the forest was, and the trees; only we were changing. We

said good-bye to it with every step, wondering how life would be without it; for its own part, it was insensitive and innocent, standing silent and raggedly beautiful as we bumped our way out of it for the very last time, bound (how strange it then seemed!) for that distant grey city of the north which claims us as her own.

Further Reading

Garner, R. L. *Gorillas and Chimpanzees*. London, 1896.

Harrisson, B. *Orang-utan*. London, 1962.

Schaller, G. B. *The Year of the Gorilla*. Chicago, 1964.

Stanley, H. M. *The Great Forest of Central Africa; Its Cannibals and Pygmies*. London, 1890.

Yerkes, R., and Yerkes, A. *The Great Apes*. New Haven, 1929.

Also mentioned in the text:

Baskerville, R. *The King of the Snakes*. London, 1922.

Beattie, J. *Bunyoro*. New York, 1960.

Churchill, W. S. *My African Journey*. Neville Spearman and Holland Press, 1908 & 1962.

Eggeling, W. J. "Observations on the Ecology of the Budongo Rain Forest, Uganda." *Journal of Ecology*, 1947.

Fabre, J. H. *The Sacred Beetle*. New York, 1918.

Johnston, H. *The Uganda Protectorate*. London, 1902.

Livingstone, D. *The Last Journals of David Livingstone in Central Africa*. London, 1874.

Moorehead, A. *No Room in the Ark*. London, 1959.

GLOSSARY

List of Latin names of some species referred to in the text.

adder, night	*Causus rhombeatus*
ant, safari	*Dorylus* sp.
baboon	*Papio anubis*
bamboo	*Arundinaria alpina*
banana, wild	*Musa* sp.
barkcloth tree	*Ficus natalensis*
bat, fruit	*Pteropodidae*
beetle, black dung	*Carabidae*
beetle, goliath	*Goliathus goliathus*
beetle, metallic green dung (jewel)	*Buprestidae*
boomslang, green	*Dispholidus typus*
buffalo, black	*Cyncerus caffer*
buffalo, red Congo	*Cyncerus nanus*
bush-baby	*Galago demidoffi*
bush-buck	*Tragelaphus scriptus*
bush-pig	*Potamochoerus porcus*
butterfly, crimson-winged	*Cymothoe* sp.
butterfly, indigo-winged	*Precis* sp.
butterfly, swallowtail	*Papilionidae*
chimpanzee	*Pan troglodytes schweinfurthii*
cicada	*Cicadidae*, probably *Platypleurinae*
civet	*Viverra civetta*
cobra, black-lipped	*Naja melanoleuca*
cork tree	*Erythrina* sp.
cormorant	*Phalacrocorax* sp.
crane, crowned	*Balearica regulorum*
dove, blue-spotted wood	*Turtur afer*
duiker, blue	*Cephalophus monticolus*
duiker, red	*Cephalophus natalensis*
egret, yellow-billed	*Mesophoyx intermedius*
elephant	*Loxodonta africana*
everlasting flowers	*Helichrysum nandense*
firefly	*Telephoridae*
fish-eagle	*Cuncuma vocifer*
fly, buttress	*Trentopohlia* sp.
fly, elephant	*Tabanus xanthomelas*
fly, lantern	*Zanna tenebrosa*
fly, red-eyed (Congo floor maggot)	*Auchmeromyia luteola*
fly-catcher, black	*Melaenornis edolioides*
francolin	*Francolinus* sp.
francolin, Nahan's forest	*Francolinus nahani*
frog, tree	*Hyperolius* sp.

gorilla	*Gorilla gorilla beringei*
guinea-fowl, crested	*Guttera edouardi*
guinea-fowl, tufted	*Numida meleagris*
hawk-eagle, long-crested	*Lophoaëtus occipitalis*
heron	*Ardea* sp.
hippopotamus	*Hippopotamus amphibius*
hog, red river	*Potamochoerus porcus*
hornbill, black-and-white casqued	*Bycanistes subcylindricus*
hornbill, white-thighed	*Bycanistes albotibialis*
horse-fly	*Tabanus besti*
hyrax, tree	*Dendrohyrax arboreus*
"igeria" tree	*Pseudospondias microcarpa*
ironwood tree	*Cynometra alexandri*
kingfisher, pied	*Ceryle rudis*
kob, Uganda	*Kobus thomasi*
leopard	*Panthera pardus*
lichen	*Usnea* sp.
lion	*Panthera leo*
mahogany trees	*Khaya anthotheca, Entandrophragma cylindricum, E. utile, E. Angolense*
mamba	*Dendroaspis* sp.
mantis	*Mantis religiosa*
marabou stork	*Leptoptilos crumeniferus*
monkey, black-and-white colobus	*Colobus abyssinicus*
monkey, blue	*Cercopithecus mitis stuhlmanni*
monkey, golden	*Cercopithecus mitis kandti*
monkey, redtail	*Cercopithecus ascanius*
monkey, vervet	*Cercopithecus aethiops*
moth, emperor	*Saturnidae*
"mpungu" tree	*Chrysophyllum perpulchrum*
"mujgangoma" tree	*Cordia millenii*
"mukunyu" trees	*Ficus mucuso, F. capensis, F. sycomorus*
"mumule" tree	*Holoptelea grandis*
"munyama" tree	*Khaya anthotheca*
"muvule" tree	*Chlorophora excelsa*
"muyati" tree	*Mildbraediodendron excelsum*
"ngrube" tree	*Melanodiscus* sp. nov.
"nyakatoma" trees	*Morus lactea, Ficus natalensis,* and other *Ficus* spp.
pangolin	*Manis tricuspis*
parrot, grey	*Psittacus erithacus*
pelican	*Pelecanus* sp.
porcupine	*Hystrix africae-australis*
potto	*Periodicticus potto*
python	*Python sebae*
rat, edible	*Thryonomys swinderianus*
rattan	*Calamus* sp.

robin-chat, white-browed   *Cossypha heuglini*
roller, blue-throated   *Eurystomus gularis*
roller, broad-billed   *Eurystomus glaucurus*

shrew, elephant   *Rhynchocyon cirnei*
snail-slug   *Testicella* sp.
snake, olive house   *Boaedon lineatum*
starling, purple-headed glossy   *Lamprocolius purpureiceps*
stick insect   *Phasmidae*

termite, rustling   *Macrotermitinae*
termite, savannah   *Macrotermes bellicosus*
tortoise, land   *Kinixys* sp.
touraco, black-billed   *Tauraco schütii*

viper, gaboon   *Bitis gabonicus*

wart-hog   *Phacochoerus aethiopicus*
water-buck   *Kobus defassa*

yellow-bill   *Ceuthmochares aereus*

Vernon Reynolds and his wife spent eight months in the Budongo rainforest of Uganda studying chimpanzees in the wild. Prior to this, for his doctorate degree in anthropology from the University of London, he spent many months studying the social behaviour of a colony of rhesus monkeys at Whipsnade Zoo in England. A member of the Royal Anthropological Institute, the Zoological Society of London, and the Association for the Study of Animal Behaviour, he was formerly a fellow at the Center for Advanced Study in the Behavioral Sciences at Stanford, California. He is the author of several articles in scientific and popular journals and, with his wife and young daughter, lives in London.

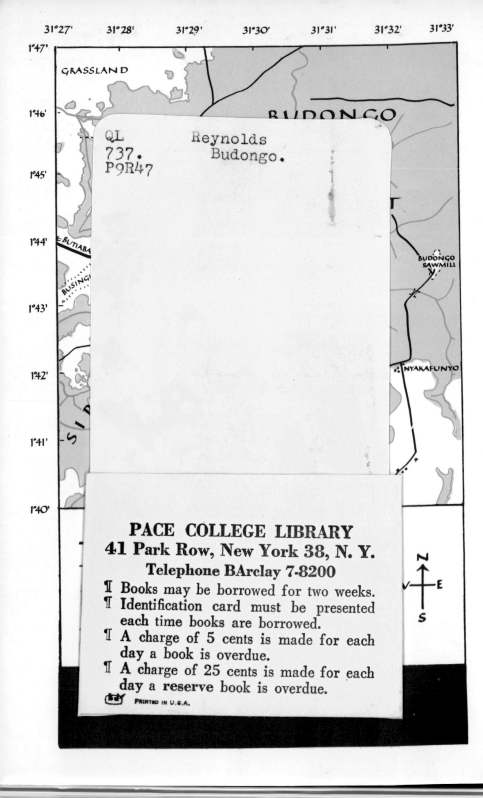